INSTITUTE OF DEVELOPMENT STUDIES

RURAL APPRAISAL: RAPID, RELAXED AND PARTICIPATORY

by

Robert Chambers

DP 311

October 1992

The term Participatory Rural Appraisal (PRA) describes a growing family of approaches and methods to enable local people to share, enhance and analyse their knowledge of life and conditions, to plan and to act. PRA flows from and owes much to activist participatory research, agroecosystem analysis, applied anthropology, field research on farming systems, and rapid rural appraisal (RRA). In RRA information is more elicited and extracted by outsiders; in PRA it is more shared and owned by local people. The behaviour and attitudes of outsider facilitators are crucial, including relaxing not rushing, showing respect, 'handing over the stick', and being self-critically aware. Modes of investigation, sharing and analysis are open-ended, and often visual, by groups, and through comparisons. Among many applications, PRA has been used in natural resources management (soil and water conservation, forestry, fisheries, wildlife, village planning etc), agriculture, programmes for the poor, health and food security. Evidence to date shows high validity and reliability in information shared by rural people through PRA. Dangers include faddism, rushing, formalism, ruts, and rejection. Challenges in spread include quality assurance and institutional change. Potentials include farmers' own farming systems research, substituting for surveys, spread by villagers, and support for the paradigm shift towards decentralization, local diversity, and empowerment of the poorer.

ISBN 0 903715 84 8

Themes: agriculture and rural problems; environment; health

ACKNOWLEDGEMENTS

I am grateful to the Ford Foundation, the Overseas Development Administration and the Swedish international Development Authority for support for the writing of this paper, and to Tony Dunn, James Mascarenhas and Jules Pretty for detailed and helpful comments on the draft. Many others have contributed in ways too numerous to mention. I thank them all. Responsibility for errors of omission, fact and judgement rests with me alone.

CONTENTS

		Page
INTRODUCTION		1
1	SOME SOURCES OF PRA	1
	1.1 ACTIVIST PARTICIPATORY RESEARCH	2
	1.2 AGROECOSYSTEM ANALYSIS	4
	1.3 APPLIED ANTHROPOLOGY	4
	1.4 FIELD RESEARCH ON FARMING SYSTEMS	5
	1.5 RAPID RURAL APPRAISAL	6
2	FROM RRA TO PRA	9
3	DEFINITION OF PRA	12
4	THE PRINCIPLES OF PRA	13
	A PRINCIPLES SHARED BY RRA AND PRA	14
	B ADDITIONAL PRINCIPLES STRESSED IN PRA	15
5	THE MENU OF METHODS OF RRA AND PRA	15
6	SIX 'DISCOVERIES' OF PRA	19
	6.1 VILLAGERS' KNOWLEDGE AND CAPABILITIES	20
	6.2 RELAXED RAPPORT	21
	6.3 DIAGRAMMING AND VISUAL SHARING	22
	6.4 SEQUENCES	23
	6.5 TRAINING AND REORIENTATION FOR OUTSIDERS	25
	6.6 SHARING AND SPREAD	26
7	UTILITY: PRACTICAL APPLICATIONS	27
	7.1 NATURAL RESOURCES MANAGEMENT	28
	7.2 AGRICULTURE	29
	7.3 PROGRAMMES FOR EQUITY	29
	7.4 HEALTH AND NUTRITION	29

Page

8 VALIDITY AND RELIABILITY 31
8.1 FARM AND HOUSEHOLD SURVEYS 33
8.2 RANKING 35
8.3 PARTICIPATORY VILLAGE CENSUSES 37
8.4 RAINFALL DATA 37

9 REVERSALS AND REALITY 39
9.1 REVERSALS OF MODES 40
a FROM CLOSED TO OPEN 40
b FROM INDIVIDUAL TO GROUP 41
c FROM VERBAL TO VISUAL 41
d FROM COUNTING TO COMPARING 44
9.2 REVERSALS OF DOMINANCE: FROM EXTRACTING TO EMPOWERING 44
9.3 FROM RESERVE TO RAPPORT, FROM TEDIUM TO FUN 46

10 EXPLAINING OUR PAST IGNORANCE 47

11 DANGERS 49

12 FRONTIERS, CHALLENGES AND POTENTIALS 51
12.1 BEYOND FARMING SYSTEMS RESEARCH (FSR) 51
12.2 POLICY RESEARCH AND CHANGE 52
12.3 PERSONAL BEHAVIOUR, ATTITUDES AND LEARNING 54
12.4 SPREAD WITH QUALITY ASSURANCE 55
12.5 EMPOWERMENT AND EQUITY 56
12.6 SUBSTITUTING FOR SURVEYS 58
12.7 SPREAD BY VILLAGERS 60
12.8 PRA IN INSTITUTIONS 61

13 THE PARADIGMATIC SIGNIFICANCE OF PRA 64

ABBREVIATIONS AND ADDRESSES 68

REFERENCES 69

Page

APPENDIX A: SOURCES OF INFORMATION 85

APPENDIX B: START, STUMBLE, SELF-CORRECT, SHARE 88

RURAL APPRAISAL: RAPID, RELAXED AND PARTICIPATORY

INTRODUCTION

The past decade has witnessed more shifts in the rhetoric of rural development than in its practice. These shifts include the now familiar reversals from top-down to bottom-up, from centralized standardization to local diversity, and from blueprint to learning process. Linked with these, there have also been small beginnings of changes in modes of learning. The move here is away from extractive survey questionnaires and towards participatory appraisal and analysis in which more and more the activities previously appropriated by outsiders are instead carried out by local rural or urban people themselves.

In these changes, a part has been played by two closely related families of approaches and of methods, often referred to as Rapid Rural Appraisal (RRA) which spread in the 1980s, and its further evolution into Participatory Rural Appraisal (PRA) which has come about fast and begun to spread in the 1990s. The purposes of this paper are to outline the origins, principles, approaches, methods and applications of both RRA and PRA; and for PRA, to explore and assess its strengths, weaknesses, potentials and paradigmatic significance.

1 SOME SOURCES OF PRA

The approaches and methods described as PRA are evolving so fast that to propose one secure and final definition would be unhelpful. As PRA further evolves, there will be changes in what it can usefully mean. It has been called 'an approach and methods for learning about rural life and conditions from, with and by rural people'. The prepositions have sometimes been reversed in order to read 'by, with and from'. PRA is, though, more than just learning. It extends into analysis, planning and action. PRA as a term is also used to describe a variety of approaches. To cover these, a recent description is that PRA is: 'a family of approaches and methods to enable rural people to share, enhance, and analyse their knowledge of life and conditions, to plan and to act'.

PRA as it exists in the early 1990s has evolved from, draws on, and resonates with, several sources and traditions. Some of its methods do appear to be new; but some have been rediscoveries (see for example some described in Whyte 1977; Pelto and

Pelto 1978; and Rhoades 1990). In understanding what has happened, it makes no sense to try to separate out causes, effects, innovations, influences and diffusion as though they follow straight lines. In a world of continuously quicker and closer communication, transfers and sharing have become more and more rapid and untraceable. So these sources and traditions have, like flows in a braided stream, intermingled more and more over the past decade, and each also continues in several forms; but directly or indirectly all have contributed to a confluence in PRA; and as with other confluences, the flow has speeded up, and innovation and change have accelerated to cover new ground.

Five streams which stand out as sources and parallels to PRA are, in alphabetical order:

- activist participatory research
- agroecosystem analysis
- applied anthropology
- field research on farming systems
- rapid rural appraisal

1.1 ACTIVIST PARTICIPATORY RESEARCH

The term 'activist participatory research' is used to refer to a family of approaches and methods which use dialogue and participatory research to enhance people's awareness and confidence, and to empower their action. Activist participatory research in this sense owes much to the work and inspiration of Paulo Freire, to his book *Pedagogy of the Oppressed* (1968), and to the practice and experience of conscienciization in Latin America. The Freirian theme, that poor and exploited people can and should be enabled to conduct their own analysis of their own reality has been widely influential, even though it has remained a minority view among development professionals as a whole. Two related schools have been known as participatory research, and participatory action research (PAR).

Participatory research has been associated with the adult education movement since at least 1975 (*Convergence* 1975; 1981; 1988: 3). Regional networks were set up. An African regional Workshop on Participatory Research was held in Tanzania in 1979 (Kassam and Mustafa 1982). In India, the Society for Participatory Research in Asia (SPR in Asia 1982) has sought to spread the philosophy and practice of participatory research. Participatory research has been conducted in widely differing conditions (Rahman 1984). For example, in Bangladesh, as recorded in *The Net* (BRAC 1983), poor and powerless people took part in investigation and analysis of the power structure in ten villages, and of how benefits directed towards them by the Government were intercepted by the local elite. In the United States, the Highlander Centre in rural Appalachia has worked to enable underprivileged communities to gain confidence in their own knowledge and abilities, and to take political action (Gaventa and Lewis 1991).

For its part, participatory action research (PAR) has been parallel and overlapping with participatory research, and has had strong associations with industry and agriculture (Whyte 1991).

Activist participatory research has taken different forms and has been practised by people with a range of ideological positions, from radical crypto-paternalism to open-ended facilitation. Its special focus on the underprivileged and on political action has threatened established interests, whether political or professional, and limited its spread. In practice, much PRA has similarly been concerned with poverty and equity. Compared with most activist participatory research, PRA has entailed less extended verbal dialogue, more visual analysis, and a more diverse repertoire of methods.

The contributions of the activist participatory research stream to PRA have been more through concepts than methods. Key commonly shared ideas and imperatives that stand out are:

- poor people are creative and capable, and can and should do much of their own investigation, analysis and planning

- outsiders have a role as convenors, catalysts and facilitators

- the weak should be empowered

1.2 AGROECOSYSTEM ANALYSIS

Agroecosystem analysis (Conway 1985,1986,1987) was developed in Thailand from 1978 onwards, initially at the University of Chiang Mai, by Gordon Conway and his colleagues (Gypmantasiri et al. 1980). It spread first through Southeast Asia and then elsewhere. Drawing on systems and ecological thinking, it has combined analysis of systems and system properties (productivity, stability, sustainability, and equitability) with pattern analysis of space (maps and transects), time (seasonal calendars and long-term trends), flows and relationships (flow, causal, Venn and other diagrams), relative values (bar diagrams of relative sources of income etc), and decisions (decision trees and other decision diagrams). The approach was further developed by Conway and others with the Aga Khan Rural Support Programme (Pakistan) for cost-effective application in villages in Northern Pakistan, where it took a form which led quickly to identification and assessment of practical hypotheses for action.

Agroecosystem analysis was so powerful and practical that it quickly overlapped with and contributed to much RRA. In some cases, either or both labels could be used to describe what was done. Some of the major contributions of agroecosystem analysis to current RRA and PRA have been:

- transects (systematic walks and observation)

- informal mapping (sketch maps drawn on site)

- diagramming (seasonal calendars, flow and causal diagrams, bar charts, Venn or 'chapati' diagrams)

- innovation assessment (scoring and ranking different actions)

1.3 APPLIED ANTHROPOLOGY

Social anthropology in its classical forms has been concerned more with understanding than with changing, but especially in the 1980s, applied anthropology, and development anthropology, became more recognized as legitimate and useful activities. In the USA, the Institute for Development Anthropology established a network and a regular Bulletin. A very few social anthropologists found their way into the International Agricultural Research Centres, where they had an influence disproportionate to their tiny numbers, and the social anthropologists in aid agencies rose in numbers and status, though they were still few. Social anthropologists helped development professionals generally better to appreciate the richness and validity of rural people's knowledge (e.g. IDS 1979; Brokensha, Warren and Werner 1980), and to distinguish the etic - the outsider's mental frame, categories and world view, and the emic - those of the insider. And *The Art of the Informal Agricultural Survey* (1982), by Robert Rhoades, a social anthropologist at the International Potato Center in Peru, was widely read and influential far beyond the informal form of its publication.

In one methodological stream, the approaches of social anthropology were adopted in health and nutrition in rapid assessment procedures (RAP) (Scrimshaw and Hurtado 1987) and in rapid ethnographic assessment (REA) (Bentley **et al.** 1988), which variously used conversations, observation, informal interviews, and focus groups.

PRA represents an extension and application of social anthropological insights, approaches and methods, cross-fertilized with others. Some of the many insights and contributions coming from and shared with social anthropology have been:

- the idea of field learning as flexible art rather than rigid science
- the value of field residence, unhurried participant-observation, and conversations
- the importance of attitudes, behaviour and rapport
- the emic-etic distinction
- the validity of indigenous technical knowledge

1.4 FIELD RESEARCH ON FARMING SYSTEMS

Field research on farming systems, whether by social anthropologists, geographers, agricultural economists or biological scientists, has revealed the complexity, diversity and rationality of much apparently untidy and unsystematic farming practice. D.G.R. Belshaw at Makerere in the 1960s, David Norman and his colleagues at Ahmadu

Bello University in Northern Nigeria in the 1970s, and Richard Harwood in Thailand (Harwood 1979) were among those who showed the good sense of practices like mixed cropping (e.g. Norman 1975). Farming systems research (FSR) (Gilbert **et al.** 1980; Shaner **et al.** 1982; FSSP 1987) systematized methods for investigating, understanding, and prescribing for farming system complexity, but sometimes bogged down in ponderous surveys and data overload.

A parallel stream of research drew attention to farmers' capabilities. Stephen Biggs in describing 'informal R & D' (1980), Paul Richards in his classic *Indigenous Agricultural Revolution* (1985), and Roland Bunch in *Two Ears of Corn* (1985) were among those who showed and recognized that farmers were experimenters. Farmers' participation in agricultural research became a focus (e.g. Farrington 1988; Farrington and Martin 1988; Chambers, Pacey and Thrupp 1989; Ashby 1990). Clive Lightfoot and his colleagues pioneered analytical and flow diagramming by farmers (e.g Lightfoot **et al.** 1991). In the latter 1980s and early 1990s it has been increasingly recognized that farmers should and could play a much greater part in agricultural research.

So field research on farming systems contributed especially to the appreciation and understanding of:

- the complexity, diversity and risk-proneness of many farming systems
- the knowledge, professionalism and rationality of small and poor farmers
- their experimental mindset and behaviour
- their ability to conduct their own analyses

1.5 RAPID RURAL APPRAISAL

The philosophy, approaches and methods known as rapid rural appraisal (RRA) began to emerge in the late 1970s. Workshops held at the IDS on rural development tourism (1977), indigenous technical knowledge (1978), and RRA itself (1978,1979) were only some among the parallel moves in different parts of the world in search of better ways for outsiders to learn about rural life and conditions. RRA can be seen to have had three main origins.

The first was dissatisfaction with the biases, especially the anti-poverty biases, of rural development tourism - the phenomenon of the brief rural visit by the urban-based professional. These biases were recognized as spatial (visits near cities, on roadsides, and to the centres of villages to the neglect of peripheries); project (where projects were being undertaken, often with special official attention and support); person (meeting men more than women, elites more than the poor, the users more than the non-users of services, and so on); seasonal (going in the dry and cool rather than hot and wet seasons which are often worse for poor rural people); and diplomatic (where the outsider does not wish to cause offence by asking to meet poor people or see bad conditions). All these could combine to hide the worst poverty and deprivation.

The second origin of RRA was disillusion with the normal processes of questionnaire surveys and their results. Again and again, over many years and in many places (see e.g. Moris 1970), the experience had been that questionnaire surveys tended to be long-drawn-out, tedious, a headache to administer, a nightmare to process and write up, inaccurate and unreliable in data obtained, leading to reports, if any, which were long, late, boring, misleading, difficult to use, and anyway ignored.

The third origin was more positive. More cost-effective methods of learning were sought. This was helped by the growing recognition by development professionals of the painfully obvious fact that rural people were themselves knowledgeable on many subjects which touched their lives. What became known as indigenous technical knowledge (ITK) (IDS 1979; Brokensha, Warren and Werner 1980) was then increasingly seen to have richness and value for practical purposes. One major question, as it seemed then, was how more effectively to tap ITK as a source of information for analysis and use by outsider professionals.

In the late 1970s, though, most of those professionals who were inventing and using methods which were quicker and more cost-effective than 'respectable' questionnaire surveys, were reluctant to write about what they did, fearing for their professional credibility. They felt compelled to conform to standard statistical norms, however costly and crude their applications, and obliged in their reports and publications to use conventional methods, categories and measures. In a classic statement, Michael Collinson (1981) described how he would take only a week to conduct an exploratory survey to identify agricultural research priorities, but would then feel obliged to follow this with a formal verification survey which represented the major commitment of professional time and funds. This more costly exercise had always confirmed the exploratory survey but 'the numbers which this formal survey provides are the only hard evidence produced by the diagnostic process. This is extremely important in convincing 'the Establishment'...' (ibid.: 444). To convince, the researcher had to be conservative; but the process was costly and decisions and action were delayed.

In the 1980s, in some places, this situation was transformed. The family of approaches and methods known as Rapid Rural Appraisal (RRA) gained increasing acceptance. It began to be seen that it had its own principles and rigour (Chambers 1980; Belshaw 1981; Carruthers and Chambers 1981). In the early 1980s, RRA was argued to be cost-effective, especially for gaining timely information, but still with some sense that it might only be a second-best. But by the mid-1980s, the RRA approaches and methods, when properly conducted, were more and more eliciting a range and quality of information and insights inaccessible through more traditional methods. Except when rushed and unself-critical, RRA came out better by criteria of cost-effectiveness, validity and reliability when it was compared with more conventional methods (see Section 8). In many contexts and for many purposes, RRA, when well done, showed itself to be not a second-best but a best.

In establishing the methods and principles of RRA many people and institutions took part. No account can do justice to them, and with imperfect knowledge there is no avoiding significant omissions. An earlier attempt to list countries where RRA had been developed identified 12 in Africa, eight in South and Southeast Asia, three in Latin America, three in Australasia and the Pacific, and one in Europe. Perhaps more than any other movement, agroecosystem analysis in Southeast Asia introduced new methods and established new credibility. In the mid 1980s, the University of Khon Kaen in Thailand was world leader in developing theory and methods, especially for multidisciplinary teams, and in institutionalizing RRA as a part of professional training. The International Conference on Rapid Rural Appraisal held at the University of Khon Kaen in 1985, and the published volume of papers which resulted (KKU 1987), were landmarks. The practical value of RRA was confirmed, and its underlying theory outlined (Beebe 1987; Gibbs 1987; Grandstaff and Grandstaff 1987a; Jamieson 1987). Then in the latter 1980s, RRA was further developed and disseminated through extensive training by the International Institute for

Environment and Development based in London, working with colleagues mainly in Africa and Asia, and through its publications, especially the informal publication *RRA Notes* (1988 -).

In specialized fields, too, there were parallel and overlapping developments. In health and nutrition, for example, Rapid Assessment Procedures (RAP) (Scrimshaw and Hurtado 1987) were practised in at least 20 countries. In agriculture, some practitioners of farming systems research and extension innovated with lighter, quicker methods in an RRA style. In irrigation, a small literature built up on RRA (e.g. Potten 1985; Groenfeldt 1989). And 'hard' journals published papers on RRA.

RRA began and continues as a better way for outsiders to learn. In answering the question - whose knowledge counts? - it sought, and continues to seek, to enable outsiders to gain information and insight from rural people and about rural conditions, and to do this in a more cost-effective and timely manner. It was, and remains, less exploitative than extractive questionnaire surveys where much is taken by the outsider, and little or nothing is given back. All the same, like most past farming systems research, its normal mode entails outsiders obtaining information, taking it away, and analysing it. This is a valid and useful activity which has and will continue to have its place. Depending on one's point of view and the context, the normal practice of non-participatory RRA can be described as extractive, or, more neutrally, elicitive.

2 FROM RRA TO PRA

In the mid 1980s, the words 'participation' and 'participatory' entered the RRA vocabulary. They had already a long history in rural development. To take but two examples, for some years in the 1970s and early 1980s, under the leadership of Norman Uphoff and others, Cornell University published the *Rural Development Participation Review* until USAID terminated its support, and participation was a recurrent theme in the contributions to Michael Cernea's book, edited for the World Bank, *Putting People First* (1985) which drew on experience from earlier years. It was at the 1985 Khon Kaen International Conference that participation began, albeit modestly, to be used in connection with RRA. Discussions at the Conference generated a typology of seven types of RRA (KKU 1987: 17) of which 'participatory RRA' was one. For this, the dominant purpose was seen as stimulating community awareness, with the outsider's role as catalyst. Later, in 1988, participatory RRAs were listed by the IIED team as one of four classes of RRA methodologies - the others being exploratory RRAs, topical RRAs, and monitoring RRAs (McCracken **et al.** 1988).

In 1988, there were parallel developments in Kenya and India. In Kenya, the National Environment Secretariat, in association with Clark University, conducted an RRA in Mbusanyi, a community in Machakos District which led to the adoption in September of a Village Resource Management Plan (Kabutha and Ford 1988). This was subsequently described as a Participatory Rural Appraisal, and the method outlined in two Handbooks (PID and NES 1989; NES 1980). Around the same time in 1988, the Aga Khan Rural Support Programme (India) was interested in developing participatory RRA, and invited IIED to help. Jennifer McCracken carried out a four-week consultancy with AKRSP in Gujarat in September and October 1988 during which participatory rapid rural appraisals were conducted by and with villagers and AKRSP staff in two villages (McCracken 1988). In different ways, both the Kenya and Indian experiences were seminal for understanding and for the development of PRA.

Subsequently, there was an explosion of innovation in India (for which see *RRA Notes* 13) especially but not only in the NGO sector. MYRADA, based in Bangalore, trained its senior staff in PRA in early 1990 (Ramachandran 1990), and came to play a major role in training for other NGOs and for Government. AKRSP continued to innovate and broke new ground in showing how well village volunteers could themselves be facilitators of PRA. ActionAid, Bangalore undertook a networking role. Any listing of the NGOs that pioneered at an early stage would include (in alphabetical order) ActionAid, Bangalore; Activists for Social Alternatives, Trichy; the Aga Khan Rural Support Programme (India); Krishi Gram Vikas Kendra, Ranchi; MYRADA, Bangalore; Seva Bharati, Midnapore District; SPEECH, Madurai; and Youth for Action, Hyderabad. Government organizations that received and promoted training included the Drylands Development Board, Karnataka, the District Rural Development Agencies, Andhra Pradesh, and several Forestry Departments. PRA methods were adopted by the National Academy of Administration, Mussoorie for the fieldwork of its 300-odd Indian Administrative Service probationers each year, and by the Xavier Institute of Social Services, Ranchi, which introduced PRA for the fieldwork of its students.

At the same time, cross-fertilization and spread took place internationally. The small group of the Sustainable Agriculture Programme at IIED, with support from the Ford

Foundation and SIDA, was decisively influential through its activities in Africa and Asia, and spread PRA and its methods through 30 substantial field-based training workshops in 15 countries and through publications and papers, especially *RRA Notes*. Manuals were written (e.g. McCracken et al. 1988; Gueye and Freudenberger 1990, 1991; Theis and Brady 1991). Among international NGOs, Intercooperation (Berne) and ActionAid (London) were prominent in seeking to promote PRA. Spread from India took place to Nepal from the initiative of Winrock International and to Sri Lanka on the initiative of Intercooperation. In early 1992, ActionAid, AKRSP and MYRADA were hosts in India to an International Roving PRA Workshop with 14 people from 11 countries in the South, and PRA or PRA-type activities were continuing to evolve independently in many countries.

A summary comparison of what are normally described as RRA and PRA is given in Table 1.

TABLE 1: RRA AND PRA COMPARED

	RRA	PRA
Period of major development	late 1970s, 1980s	late 1980s, 1990s
Major innovators based in	Universities	NGOs
Main users	Aid agencies Universities	NGOs Government field organizations
Key resource earlier overlooked	Local people's knowledge	Local people's capabilities
Main innovation	Methods	Behaviour
Predominant mode	Elicitive, extractive	Facilitating, participatory
Ideal objectives	Learning by outsiders	Empowerment of local people
Longer-term outcomes	Plans, projects, publications	Sustainable local action and institutions

Now, in mid-1992 as quite rapid spread is taking place of activities described as PRA, it is overdue to take stock of the principles of PRA, its methods, applications, strengths, weaknesses, potentials, and paradigmatic significance.

3 DEFINITION OF PRA

It has been a question whether it is useful to define PRA as separate from RRA.

One view is that labels do not matter. There is a plethora of labels for approaches and methods of learning about rural life and conditions. Many of the sets of practices overlap. There is continuous innovation, sharing and exchange. In this view, the only importance of a label is the sense of pride of ownership and originality which it gives, so strengthening commitment, enthusiasm and good work among its practitioners. Otherwise, there would be no point in defining an exclusive territory of activities for PRA or any other set of approaches or methods.

The opposite view is that good PRA often implies radical personal and institutional change, and that the term should not be debased by being used for anything less than this. In this view, the claim that 'PRA is a simple methodology...' (PID and NES 1989: 1) is misleading, since personal and institutional change are so rarely simple or easy. Moreover, if PRA becomes fashionable, many will label and relabel their work PRA when in fact it is still extractive rather than participatory, and when their behaviour and attitudes are unchanged.

A balanced view may be that since we are concerned here with static terms - RRA and PRA - for combinations and fluxes of activities which are far from static, and which take different forms in different places, labels can help to define what belongs where. This may serve to encourage better performance. The legitimating label of RRA has already been used quite widely to describe sloppy and bad work: see for example, a critique of a quick but heavily biased 'RRA' survey in Zambia (Pottier 1991), and some of the observations in a wide-ranging review of RRA activities in the Philippines (van Steijn 1991). The label of PRA could similarly be used to legitimate bad work; it could also be misused to describe RRA which is elicitive or extractive rather than participatory. In this view, then, it would make sense to separate out definitions of RRA as a form of data collection by outsiders who then take it away and analyse it; and PRA as more participatory, meaning that outsiders are convenors, catalysts and facilitators to enable people to undertake and share their own investigations and analysis. There is, then, a distinction between 'an RRA' and 'a PRA'. An RRA is intended for learning by outsiders. A PRA is intended to enable local people to conduct their own analysis, and often to plan and take action.

In practice there is a continuum between an RRA and a PRA. This can be understood through a description of methods. Some methods, like direct observation, and semi-structured interviewing, have been emphasized in RRA but can be a vital part of good PRA. Other methods, like participatory mapping, where local people make their own maps, and participatory diagramming, are emphasized in PRA but can also be used in an RRA mode. The continuum is illustrated in Table 2.

4 THE PRINCIPLES OF PRA

For both RRA and PRA, good performance requires that practitioners and facilitators follow basic principles. Some are fully shared, and some have been additionally emphasized in PRA

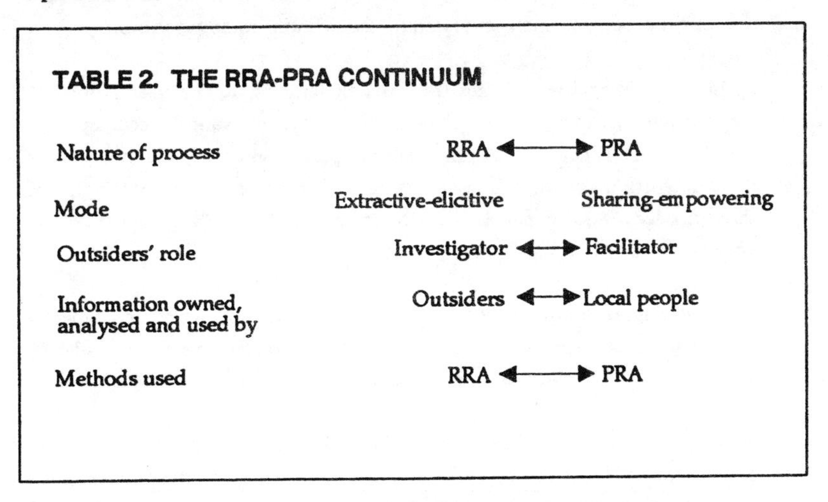

TABLE 2. THE RRA-PRA CONTINUUM

Nature of process	RRA	◄——►	PRA
Mode	Extractive-elicitive		Sharing-empowering
Outsiders' role	Investigator	◄——►	Facilitator
Information owned, analysed and used by	Outsiders	◄——►	Local people
Methods used	RRA	◄——►	PRA

Most of these principles have been induced rather than deduced: they have been elicited by trying out practices, finding what works and what does not, and then asking why. Different practitioners would list different principles underlying RRA and PRA (see e.g. Grandstaff, Grandstaff and Lovelace 1987:9-13; McCracken, Pretty and Conway 1988:12-13; Gueye and Freudenberger 1990:10-19) but most might agree to include the following:

A PRINCIPLES SHARED BY RRA AND PRA

- **a reversal of learning**, to learn from rural people, directly, on the site, and face-to-face, gaining from local physical, technical and social knowledge

- **learning rapidly and progressively**, with conscious exploration, flexible use of methods, opportunism, improvization, iteration, and crosschecking, not following a blueprint programme but being adaptable in a learning process.

- **offsetting biases**, especially those of rural development tourism, by being relaxed and not rushing, listening not lecturing, probing instead of passing on to the next topic, being unimposing instead of important, and seeking out the poorer people and women, and learning their concerns and priorities.

- **optimizing trade-offs**, relating the costs of learning to the useful truth of information, with trade-offs between quantity, relevance, accuracy and timeliness. This includes the principles of optimal ignorance - knowing what it is not worth knowing, and of appropriate imprecision - not measuring more than needed. As Keynes is reputed to have said: 'It is better to be approximately right than precisely wrong'.

- **triangulating**, meaning using a range, (sometimes three), of methods, types of information, investigators and/or disciplines to crosscheck (Grandstaff, Grandstaff and Lovelace 1987: 9-10; Gueye and Freudenberger 1991: 14-16).

- **seeking diversity**, This has been expressed in terms of seeking variability rather than averages (Beebe 1987: 53-54), and has been described in Australia as the principle of maximum diversity, or 'maximizing the diversity and richness of information' (Dunn and McMillan 1991: 5,8). This can involve sampling in a non-statistical sense. It goes beyond the crosschecking of triangulation; for defined broadly it deliberately looks for, notices and investigates contradictions, anomalies, and differentness.

B ADDITIONAL PRINCIPLES STRESSED IN PRA

To these shared principles, PRA adds others:

- **facilitating - they do it:** facilitating investigation, analysis, presentation and learning by rural people themselves, so that they present and own the outcomes, and also learn. This has been expressed as 'handing over the stick' (or pen or chalk). This often entails an outsider starting a process and then sitting back or walking away, and not interviewing or interrupting.

- **self-critical awareness and responsibility:** meaning that facilitators are continuously examining their behaviour, and trying to do better. This includes embracing error - welcoming error as an opportunity to learn to do better; and using one's own best judgement at all times, meaning accepting personal responsibility rather than vesting it in a manual or a rigid set of rules.

- **sharing** of information and ideas between rural people, between them and facilitators, and between different facilitators, and sharing field camps, training and experiences between different organizations.

All these principles are behavioural, since they are applied in practice by people doing things. But those shared by RRA and PRA are more epistemological; while those of PRA are more personal. And this difference indicates the new emphasis placed in PRA on the behaviour and attitudes of outsiders in their interactions with rural people, an emphasis which could usefully be part of future RRA as well as PRA.

5 THE MENU OF METHODS OF RRA AND PRA

In its early days, RRA seemed to be largely organized commonsense. During the 1980s, though, creative ingenuity was applied and more methods borrowed, adapted and invented, many with a more participatory mode. A summary listing of headings can give some indication of the types of methods being used in mid-1992 without being exhaustive. All the methods can be used in both RRA and PRA, but some are more emphasized in one than the other.

- **secondary sources** - such as files, reports, maps, aerial photographs, articles and books

- **do-it-yourself:** asking to be taught to perform village tasks - transplanting, weeding, ploughing, field-levelling, drawing water, collecting wood, washing clothes, thatching...

- **key informants:** enquiring who are the experts and seeking them out

- **semi-structured interviews.** This has been regarded by some as the 'core' of good RRA (Grandstaff and Grandstaff 1987b). It can entail having a mental or written checklist, but being open-ended and following up on the unexpected. Increasingly it is using participatory visual as well as traditional verbal methods

- **groups** of various kinds (casual; specialist/focus; deliberately structured; community/neighbourhood). Group interviews and activities are part of many of the methods

- **sequences or chains of interviews** - from group to group; or from group to key informant; or a sequence of key informants, each expert on a different stage of a process (eg men on ploughing, women on transplanting and weeding...) etc

- **they do it:** villagers and village residents as investigators and researchers - women, poor people, school teachers, volunteers, students, farmers, village specialists. They do transects, observe, interview other villagers, analyse data, and present the results

- **participatory mapping and modelling,** in which people use the ground, floor or paper to make social, demographic, health, natural resource (soils, trees and forests, water resources etc) or farm maps, or construct three-dimensional models of their land

- **participatory analysis of aerial photographs** (often best at 1:5000) to identify soil type, land conditions, land tenure etc

- **transect walks** - systematically walking with informants through an area, observing, asking, listening, discussing, identifying different zones, local technologies, introduced technologies, seeking problems, solutions and opportunities, and mapping and diagramming resources and findings

- **time lines**: chronologies of events, listing major remembered events in a village with approximate dates

- **trend analysis**: people's accounts of the past, of how things close to them have changed, ecological histories, changes in land use and cropping patterns, changes in customs and practices, changes and trends in population, migration, fuels used, education, health, credit... and the causes of changes and trends

- **ethno biographies**: local histories of a crop, an animal, a tree, a pest, a weed...

- **seasonal diagramming** - by major season or by month to show days and distribution of rain, amount of rain or soil moisture, crops, agricultural labour, non-agricultural labour, diet, food consumption, types of sickness, prices, animal fodder, fuel, migration, income, expenditure, debt etc

- **livelihood analysis** - stability, crises and coping, relative income, expenditure, credit and debt, multiple activities...

- **participatory diagramming** - of flows, causality, quantities, trends, rankings, scorings - in which people make their own diagrams - systems diagrams, bar diagrams, pie charts etc.. 'Chapati' or Venn diagramming is one form, a method for identifying individuals and institutions important in and for a community, and their relationships

- **wellbeing or wealth ranking** - identifying clusters of households according to wellbeing or wealth, including those considered poorest or worst off (*RRA Notes* 15)

- **analysis of difference**, especially by gender, social group, wealth/poverty, occupation and age. Identifying differences between groups, including their problems and preferences. This includes contrast comparisons - asking one group why another is different or does something different, and vice versa

- **scoring and ranking**, especially using matrices and seeds to compare through scoring, for example different trees, or soils, or methods of soil and water conservation, or varieties of a crop

- **estimates and quantification**, often using local measures, judgements and materials such as seeds, pellets, fruits or stones as counters, sometimes combined with participatory maps and models.

- **key local indicators**, such as poor people's criteria of wellbeing

- **key probes**, questions which can lead direct to key issues such as - 'What do you talk about when you are together?' 'What new practices have you or others in this village experimented with in recent years?' 'What vegetable, tree, crop, crop variety, type of animal, tool, equipment... would you like to try out?' 'What do you do when someone's hut or house burns down?'

- **stories, portraits and case studies** such as a household history and profile, coping with a crisis, how a conflict was or was not resolved...

- **team contracts and interactions** - contracts drawn up by teams with agreed norms of behaviour; modes of interaction within teams, including changing pairs, evening discussions, mutual criticism and help, etc. (The team may be just outsiders, or a joint team with villagers)

- **presentations and analysis** - where maps, models, diagrams, and findings are presented by villagers, or by outsiders, and checked, corrected and discussed

- **participatory planning, budgetting and monitoring**, in which villagers prepare their own plans, budgets and schedules, and monitor progress

- **brainstorming**, by villagers alone, by villagers and outsiders together, or by outsiders alone

- **short, simple questionnaires** (if at all) late in the process, designed to fill dummy tables which are by then known to be needed.

- **report writing** at once, either in the field before returning to office or headquarters, or by one or more people who are designated in advance to do this immediately on completion of the RRA or PRA

6 SIX 'DISCOVERIES' OF PRA

PRA has broken new ground, but every historian knows that there is nothing new under the sun, and what appear to be 'discoveries' are often only rediscoveries. Perhaps it is safest to express this personally, and to say that for me there have been discoveries, although some of them may be old hat for others. To understand more of the background, let us look further at the contrast between traditional extractive research and RRA on the one hand, and PRA on the other.

A major difference between research and RRA which are extractive, and PRA which is participatory, is in behaviour, attitudes and roles. In extractive research and RRA the outsiders - 'we' - are dominant. We determine the agenda, obtain and take possession of information, remove it, organize and analyse it, and plan and write papers and reports. We appropriate and come to own the information. We are collectors, processors and producers of outputs. In PRA, this is largely reversed. 'We' encourage and allow 'them' to be dominant, to determine much of the agenda, to gather, express and analyse information, and to plan. We are facilitators, learners and consultants. Our activities are to establish rapport, to convene and catalyse, to enquire, to help in the use of methods, and to encourage people to choose and improvize methods for themselves. We watch, listen and learn. Metaphorically, and sometimes actually, we 'hand over the stick' of authority.

'They' then do many of the things we formerly did (and believed, often enough, that only we could do). They make maps and models; they walk transects and observe; they investigate and interview; they diagram and analyse; they present information; they plan. In consequence, they are more in command of investigation, they own and retain more of the information, and they are strongly placed to identify their priorities for action, and then to determine and control that action.

The participatory orientation of PRA has given new impetus to the development of methods. One of the delights of PRA has been the lack of blueprint. Participation generates diversity; villagers play a part in interpreting, applying, and sometimes inventing the methods themselves. Villagers and outsiders alike are encouraged to improvize in a spirit of play. What is done is different each time, the outcome of a creative interaction. In consequence, the three years to mid-1992 have witnessed many inventions, especially but not only in India and Nepal. Reviewing the participatory innovation of the past three years, six salient 'discoveries' stand out:

6.1 VILLAGERS' KNOWLEDGE AND CAPABILITIES

The first discovery is that villagers have a greater capacity to map, model, quantify and estimate, rank, score and diagram than outsiders have generally supposed them capable of.

Participatory mapping and modelling (Mascarenhas and Kumar 1991) has been a most striking finding. An earlier work on mental maps (Gould and White 1974) did not reveal the richness of detail and discrimination expressed recently by villagers in India and elsewhere through participatory mapping. A working hypothesis is that in general rural people in the South have more extensive and detailed mental maps than urban people in the North; and that given the right conditions and materials, they can express this visibly on the ground or on paper, either as maps or as three-dimensional models (for example of watersheds). They have now created many hundreds of such maps and models in at least 12 States in India, and in countries as different as Botswana, Burkina Faso (Hahn 1990), Cap Verde, Ethiopia, the Gambia, Honduras, Kenya, Nigeria, Pakistan, the Philippines, Senegal, Sri Lanka, Tanzania, Vietnam, Zambia, and Zimbabwe, either showing the huts and houses in a village (a social map) or the surrounding village area (a resources map), or combining both. Most recently they have been indicating social details, using local materials such as seeds, stones and vegetables, or markers such as bindis (the small spots Indian women place on their foreheads). These are placed on cards or on the ground on the maps or models to indicate for each household the numbers of men, women, and children, assets owned, wealth/poverty, the handicapped, immunization status, education, and other information. With an informed group or person, a participatory census of a small village can be conducted in less than an hour, and then much other information added by 'interviewing the map'. Similarly, with quantification, estimating, ranking, scoring and diagramming, when the methods and materials are right, villagers have shown themselves capable of generating and analysing information beyond far beyond normal professional expectations.

To enable these capabilities to be expressed, the principle has been to assume that people can do something until proved otherwise. It has been following that principle that participatory mapping and modelling, Venn diagramming, matrix ranking and scoring, and other methods have been 'discovered' not as one-off achievements, but as near-universals, that people appear able to use largely independently of culture or literacy. They then provide people with the occasion and means to reflect on and rank problems and opportunities as they perceive them, and to express their preferences - for improving their farming systems, for managing and using of common property resources, for better livelihoods, for health interventions, for species mixes in tree nurseries, for the qualities of new varieties of a crop, for amenities and their location, for development actions in their communities, and so on.

In all this, both methods and materials have been important in enabling villagers' capabilities to be expressed. But these in themselves are not enough.

6.2 RELAXED RAPPORT

The second discovery is that relaxed rapport between outsiders and rural people can and should be established early in the process.

Rapport is a key to facilitating participation. Relaxed rapport between outsider and villager, and some measure of trust, are minimum predisposing conditions for PRA. In the past, two extreme types of interaction between outsiders and rural people have missed major opportunities: the rushed and unselfcritical rural development tourist has had neither the time and nor the sensitivity to get far beyond formal mutual misunderstanding; and the pure social anthropologist has allowed so much time and shown such sensitivity that she or he has come to believe that only through prolonged residence can good rapport and good insights be gained. The two 'cultures' - of rushed visitor, and of resident expert - have conspired to conceal the potential for gaining rapport early and well, and early enough and well enough for the honest and accurate sharing of detailed knowledge and values. To a hardened 'old hand' at rural development tourism (the senior official: 'I was born and brought up in a village', 'I am a farmer myself' 'You can't pull the wool over my eyes') this might seem unnecessary: he (most are men) knows it all and has an automatic good rapport with all rural people. To a seasoned social anthropologist (the university professor: 'It took a year before they would tell me that...') this might seem an affront:

it would be unfair if others in a short time could achieve what had taken her (relatively more are women) so long. For anyone who has endured and struggled through months of residence and participant-observation to achieve rapport and insight, learning a new language and living a new life, it could seem unlikely and even unwelcome, that other outsiders should find ways to establish rapport and glean good insights more quickly and with pleasure, participation and fun.

Empirically, though, the finding again and again with PRA is that if the initial behaviour and attitudes of outsiders are relaxed and right, and if the process can start, the methods of PRA themselves foster further rapport. Early actions by outsiders can include transparent honesty about who they are and what they are doing; and participation in village activities, especially being taught and performing village tasks. Personal demeanour counts, showing humility, respect, patience, and interest in what villagers have to say and show; wandering around and not rushing; and paying attention, listening, watching and not interrupting. Then villagers quickly lose themselves in activities such as participatory mapping and modelling and matrix scoring. In contrast with questionnaires, they do not have a sense that information is being handed over and to be taken away. It is theirs. They own it, but share it. They often enjoy the creativity of what they are doing, and what they see and learn through it. The pleasure, fun and utility of what they have been helped to start doing express themselves in rapport. By reinforcing rapport, PRA methods thus sustain and strengthen the participatory process of which they are a part.

6.3 DIAGRAMMING AND VISUAL SHARING

The third discovery is the popularity and power of participatory diagramming and visual sharing.

Diagramming and visual sharing are common elements in much PRA. With a questionnaire survey, information is appropriated by the outsider. It is transferred from the words of the person interviewed to the paper of the questionnaire schedule where it becomes the possession of the interviewer. The learning is one-off. The information becomes personal and private, unverified, and owned by the interviewer. In contrast, with visual sharing of a map, model, diagram, or units (stones, seeds, small fruits etc) used for ranking, scoring, counting or quantification, all who are present can see, point to, discuss, manipulate and alter physical objects or representations. Triangulation takes place with people crosschecking and correcting each other. The learning is progressive. The information is visible, semi-permanent, and public, and is checked, verified, amended, added to, and owned, by the participants.

For example, in participatory mapping and modelling, villagers draw and model their villages and resources, deciding what to include, and debating, adding and modifying detail. Everyone can see what is being 'said' because it is being 'shown'. In shared diagramming, information is diagrammed to represent, for example, seasonal changes in dimensions such as rainfall, agricultural labour, income, indebtedness, food supply and migration. Paper can be used for diagrams, but the ground and other local materials have the advantage of being 'theirs', media which villagers, whether literate or non-literate, can command and alter with confidence. The diagram also presents a visible checklist or agenda which is theirs.

6.4 SEQUENCES

The fourth discovery is the power and popularity of sequences of participatory methods.

Some of the participatory methods have been known and used in the past (Rhoades 1990). There are now some new ones, but perhaps more striking is the power of combinations and sequences which has been revealed (Shah 1991). To take some examples:

- with participatory mapping, villagers draw not one, but several maps, which become successively more detailed and useful, or which present new and complementary information. (The same can apply with other methods)

- social mapping provides a basis for household listings, and for indicating population, social group, health and other household characteristics. This can lead to identification of key informants, and then to discussions with them. (This is a useful sequence in many topic RRAs and PRAs)

- a participatory resource map leads to planning transect walks in which villagers who made the map act as guides for outsiders. The transects in turn lead to the identification and discussion of problems and opportunities, which then lead to listing and ranking options or 'best bets'.

- a participatory resource map of an area of degraded forest, and a rootstock census of quadrats in the forest carried out by villagers, leads to a calculation of numbers of trees to be planted; and debate and analysis leads to people's decisions about the proportions of different trees to be planted, and the numbers required in tree nurseries (M. Shah forthcoming)

- a village social map provides an up-to-date household listing which is then used for wellbeing or wealth ranking of households which leads in turn to focus groups with different categories of people who then express their different preferences, leading to discussion, negotiation and reconcilation of priorities (combining Mukherjee 1992 and Swift and Umar 1991)

- matrix scoring or ranking elicits villagers' criteria of goodness and badness of a class of things (trees, vegetables, fodder grasses, varieties of a crop or animal, sources of credit, market outlets, fuel types...) which leads into discussion of preferences and actions.

Longer sequences have been devised and used in full PRAs. In Kenya these have been part of a stepwise sequence (PID and NES 1989). In India, for example with the Aga Khan Rural Support Programme, the sequences have been less codified and more in a style of systematic improvization, though with specialized sequences for example for appraisal, planning and action with degraded forests, or with identifying and working with the poorest.

The power of such sequences is fourfold. First, the commitment of participants increases, making further action more likely, more spontaneous, and more sustainable. Second, sequences triangulate, and reveal errors or omissions in earlier presentations (see e.g. Pretty et al. 1992). Third, the different activities interact cumulatively, each activity adding a dimension and details which qualify and enrich others, so that taken together the whole becomes more than the sum of the parts. Fourth, all concerned learn through the process, through people sharing what they know, through observation and through analysis. In such ways as these, participatory methods fit well with a flexible learning process approach which is even more open-ended and adaptable than much earlier RRA; and they have the advantage that they usually enable villagers to use their own categories and criteria, to generate their own agenda, and to assess and indicate their own priorities.

6.5 TRAINING AND REORIENTATION FOR OUTSIDERS

The fifth discovery is that for some outsiders, initial training and reorientation need not take long before they can go off and practice.

The duration of training or familiarization covers a wide range. To date, Universities have usually taken longer and NGOs and Government shorter periods. RRA training conducted at the University of Khon Kaen in Thailand in 1990 took six weeks, which was considered inadequate (Grandstaff **et al.** 1990). PRA training at Egerton University in Kenya in 1990 took three weeks, and is being repeated. At the other extreme, in one case in India, slides of participatory mapping and 'handing over the stick' were shown for about an hour, and both were then adapted and adopted by a large NGO. In between these extremes, there have been workshops and training of half a day, a day, two days, and so on up to ten days.

Face-to-face field experience is the key. The classroom insulates and inhibits; the field exposes and liberates. No one can learn to swim without entering the water. Participants in training often say they are not ready, that they need another day, more practice, before starting. But, applying the principle of optimal unpreparedness, it is usually best to start sooner than seems safe or sensible to newcomers; not to wait, but to start, stumble, self-correct, and then share.

On these lines, much PRA training in India has taken three to five days spent camping in or near a village (e.g. Ramanchandran 1990; Devavaram **et al.** 1991; Jayakaran 1991; Joseph and Joseph 1991; Kumar 1991; Mascarenhas 1992). The camp usually entails two processes: training and learning for the team of outsiders, using various methods; and a participatory process which is 'for real', leading to plans developed by and with villagers. Staying a number of nights in the village intensifies and concentrates the experience. Attention is paid to outsiders' behaviour and attitudes. Villagers are encouraged to map, diagram, participate in transect walks, and plan. The major aim of the training for the outsiders is to facilitate changes in perception and action, listening not lecturing, learning progressively, embracing error, being critically self-aware, and themselves participating, for example reversing roles by being taught by villagers to perform village tasks. For some outsiders, especially those who have had a strictly formal professional training, this can threaten trauma. They deserve sympathetic understanding, and no significant change may take place. For some, though, there opens up a new range of possibilities and a sense of freedom to experiment and innovate. It is then not necessary to be trained in all the methods. They can be tried, improvised and adapted subsequently, and new ones invented. The outsider's creativity is released, as well as that of the villager.

Another approach is to smuggle in participatory methods. Some professionals resist PRA approaches and methods, considering them unscientific and inappropriate. Methods which generate figures, matrices and tables can then sometimes help in getting started, and making other methods more acceptable. Robin Mearns found in Mongolia that wealth ranking was useful in this context as part of a 'hidden agenda' by giving 'every appearance of being the kind of 'hard' statistical method that Mongolian researchers and bureaucrats, like their counterparts in many parts of the world, have been professionally socialised to use and expect' (Mearns **et al.** 1992: 37). Similarly, matrix scoring for varieties of a crop provides not only fascinating information but also good-looking tables with figures. The question is whether scientists and others will be so impressed by farmers' criteria, judgements and abilities as demonstrated in matrix scoring, and by the resulting matrices, that they will go on from this method to others, and progressively become more participatory.

6.6 SHARING AND SPREAD

The last discovery concerns the importance of sharing in the culture and spread of PRA.

PRA in practice is recognized now to have three foundations: methods; behaviour and attitudes; and sharing. At first, the methods appeared the most important; then the behaviour and attitudes of outsiders were seen as primary, especially for rapport; and now the third foundation, sharing, is recognized as having grown in importance. This is partly because it has become the mode in which PRA spreads. PRA in India has a culture of sharing which owes much to MYRADA and also to other NGOs. Village camps have been open to people from other organizations. Typically, a training camp organized by an NGO will include not just its own staff but also people from other NGOs and from government. Sharing is part of the experience of the camp: sharing of information by villagers, presenting it to each other and to outsiders; sharing of ideas and experience concerning approaches and methods between outsiders and villagers; sharing of self-critical appraisal of the process among outsiders; and sharing of food by all.

If PRA is spreading through the sharing of experience and mutual learning, it is also taking different forms in different places. People and organizations are inventing their own combinations and creating their own cultures. Some emphasize one set of methods; some another. Any one method - transect walks (Mascarenhas 1990), or wellbeing ranking (*RRA Notes* 15) for example - now has several variants. To share and exchange methods and experiences, interchanges of staff are efficient, with staff of one organization spending time with other organizations in their PRAs. In all cases, also, the creativity and inventiveness of villagers can come into play. In such ways, innovations can be continuously stimulated. It is then through all forms of sharing - of training camps, of trainers, of ideas, of experiences, of methods, of innovations - that spread takes place.

7 UTILITY: PRACTICAL APPLICATIONS

The case for RRA and PRA approaches is practical. It is the experience that they work. The experiential and anecdotal evidence for the utility of well-conducted RRA and PRA is now massive, but has not been adequately drawn together and analysed.

To document the applications of RRA and PRA to date would require a separate paper and bibliography (but see for example **Agricultural Administration** (1981) volume on RRA; **IDS Bulletin** (1981); KKU 1987, especially Gibbs 1987, and the bibliography; Lovelace, Subhadhira and Simaraks, 1988; PID and NES 1989; IIED publications including cases from Cap Verde, Chile, Ecuador, Ethiopia, Fiji, the Gambia, India, Indonesia, Kenya, Pakistan, Sri Lanka, Sudan, and Zimbabwe; RRA Notes **passim**, especially Number 13 reporting experience in India; and **Forests, Trees and People News** Number 15/16, 1992. There have also been many articles (for an earlier listing see Chambers 1985: 412-4) and numerous unpublished reports).

Regarding RRA, RRA approaches and methods have been used for appraisal, analysis and research in many subject areas. These include agroecosystems; natural resources, including forestry, fisheries and the environment; irrigation; technology and innovation; health and nutrition; farming systems research and extension;

pastoralism; marketing; disaster relief; organizational assessment; social, cultural and economic conditions; and many special topics. As well as RRA, PRA has also been or could be applied to all these.

Regarding PRA, so much is being done so fast in so many places that any inventory of PRA applications made in mid-1992 will be incomplete and quickly out-of-date. However, most of the applications I know of can be separated into four types of process, and into four major sectors.

The four major **types of process** are:

- participatory appraisal and planning

- participatory implementation, monitoring and evaluation of programmes

- topic investigations

- training and orientation for outsiders and villagers

The four major **sectors** are the following. The sources are now so voluminous that only a few, and mainly very recent and accessible, references are given. For others see IDS 1992. A bibliographical review is overdue.

7.1 NATURAL RESOURCES MANAGEMENT

- watersheds, and soil and water conservation: e.g. participatory watershed planning and management (including rapid catchment analysis (Pretty 1990))

- forestry: e.g.social and community forestry; degraded forest assessment, protection, nurseries and planting; identification of tree uses; uses and marketing of minor forest products.(See e.g Case 1990; and for a strong PRA sequence M.Shah forthcoming)

- fisheries

- wildlife reserve buffer zones

- rural energy assessments, and fuel and fodder budgeting

- village plans: preparing Village Resource Management Plans (PID and NES 1990), Participatory Rural Appraisal and Planning (as developed by AKRSP), and others.

7.2 AGRICULTURE

- crops and animal husbandry, including farmer participatory research/ farming systems research by farmers

- irrigation, including rehabilitation of small-scale gravity flow irrigation systems

- markets: investigating markets and smallholder marketing potentials

7.3 PROGRAMMES FOR EQUITY

- women: participatory appraisal of problems and opportunities

- credit: identification of credit needs, sources and interventions

- selection: finding and selecting poor people for a programme, and deselecting the less poor (e.g Chandramouli 1991; *RRA Notes* 15 **passim**)

- income-earning: identification of non-agricultural income-earning opportunities

7.4 HEALTH AND NUTRITION

- health assessments and monitoring (e.g Appleton 1992; Francis, Devavaram and Erskine 1992; Joseph 1992). Applications include women's reproductive health (Tolley and Bentley 1992; Cornwall 1992), disease problem ranking (Welbourn 1992), unemployment and health (Cresswell 1992), identifying major illness, healthcare providers and costs (Joseph 1992), and planning health projects (Francis, Devavaram and Erskine 1992) (see also Heaver 1992 and *RRA Notes* 16: 101-106 for a fuller listing of actual or potential uses)

- food security and nutrition assessment and monitoring (Maxwell 1989; Appleton 1992; Buchanan-Smith 1992)

- water and sanitation assessment, planning and location

These lists are to illustrate known applications. They are by no means comprehensive, and many more applications can be expected.

For several reasons, there are still (mid-1992) few case studies of the impact of PRA. First, PRA is recent, and many PRA processes are still in their early stages. Second, responding to demand and their own sense of priorities, experienced practitioners have been mostly engaged in training and appraisal rather than monitoring and evaluation, and this emphasis is reflected in the reports they have written. Third, academic researchers have been slow to recognize what has been happening, and have rarely studied PRA.

These are conditions in which negative experiences are liable to be overlooked. More feedback is needed from whatever failures can be found, from those who have experienced PRA and not subsequently adopted it, and from organizations where attempts to introduce it have not been successful.

That said, positive evidence takes two main forms: the scale of adoption and use by organizations and individuals; and accounts of practical use.

First, the number of organizations which have to some degree adopted PRA is large and growing. The estimates which follow mainly concern agriculture and natural resources: I do not have a good sense of the scale of adoption and use in health, where PRA is also spreading locally, especially through UNICEF. NGOs which are in some places using PRA (mid-1992) must number at least a hundred, and perhaps several hundred. At least a dozen universities and training institutes have some staff who are exploring and using PRA (though almost everywhere they are a small minority) (see Section 12.8). Government and parastatal organizations, all or parts of which have espoused PRA, are a similar number. Among these, a few have sought to introduce it throughout their programmes: among others, the Soil and Water Conservation Branch of the Ministry of Agriculture in Kenya, which has officially adopted a PRA approach for its work in over 40 Districts; the Drylands Development Board in Karnataka, India; and the District Rural Development Agencies, Andhra

Pradesh, India. Government programmes with donor support are introducing PRA training and approaches, as with the ODA-supported Western Ghats programme in India, and the SIDA-supported Vietnam-Sweden Forestry Cooperation Programme in Vietnam. Actual spread and use in large field agencies, whether Government or NGO, is easily overestimated. Sometimes resistance can be expected. Much depends on personal orientation and choice, and on rewards. In smaller organizations with committed leadership, adoption is possible in a shorter time. In large organizations, it is not by administrative fiat, but by consistent high-level support, widespread training of good quality, and appropriate systems of rewards, that actual spread will take place. With those caveats, the number of people who have now chosen to use PRA as approach and process, not just PRA methods, now numbers thousands, and is growing.

Second, accounts of practical use are innumerable but scattered in a large, inaccessible, grey literature. Not surprisingly, most of this is strongly positive. All the same, few PRA processes have yet been thoroughly researched and analysed. Recent evaluations are, though, showing that where the PRA approach has been used compared with just using T and V (training and visit), a range of agricultural and economic indicators are much more favourable, such as higher agricultural yields, greater diversity of crops, reduced soil erosion and sedimentation, greater net present value and benefit: cost rations, higher land prices, and higher wage rates (pers. comm. Jules Pretty). Similar findings have been reported from the work of AKRSP in Gujarat.

A critical review of the other evidence and examples in the grey literature is overdue. There is also a huge research agenda to understand better the applications and potentials, the processes and impacts, and the shortcomings and strengths of PRA. Some of these can, however, already be assessed in terms of data validity and reliability.

8 VALIDITY AND RELIABILITY

Those who become involved with PRA tend to become enthusiastic. There can be an exhilarating sense of liberation and discovery. The presentation and analysis of detailed local knowledge in maps, models, matrices, diagrams and the like by villagers can impress outsiders deeply in a personal way which challenges preconceptions, and affects beliefs and behaviour. This is reflected in remarks of NGO staff:

After participatory social mapping	'I have been working for eight years in this village, but I never saw it like this before'
After PRA experience	'I shall never go back to questionnaires'
After PRA training	'I have been trying to get this information in this village for six months, and now we have it in two afternoons'

The experience behind these and similar statements is a fact. For those who make them, the evidence of personal experience is enough. But questions can and must be asked about less personal and experiential means of assessing the validity and reliability of PRA approaches and methods.

Validity here refers to the closeness of a finding to the reality, and reliability refers to the constancy of findings. Highly valid findings are also highly reliable, but where there is a systematic bias, reliability can be high but validity low. Validity and reliability are not absolute values. There can be trade-offs, through optimal ignorance and appropriate imprecision, where lower validity and reliability can be more cost-effective, and can enhance utility through less cost or greater relevance or timeliness.

At the outset, most large questionnaire surveys present any assessment of PRA with low standards of comparison. (Certain routinized and repeated surveys like the National Sample Survey in India are at least partial exceptions to what follows). Devastating critiques of rural questionnaire surveys have found them often badly designed, badly implemented, and badly analysed (see e.g. Moris 1970; Campbell, Shrestha and Stone 1979; Daane 1987; Gill forthcoming). All too often, questionnaire surveys are found wanting on many counts. And rarely are they subjected to full critical scrutiny.

Comparison should, though, also be made with rural questionnaire surveys which have been relatively well conducted. An example can illustrate. In 1973-4 I collaborated in a large questionnaire survey in Tamil Nadu (reported in Farmer 1977:37-44). Since I was responsible neither for the training of the investigators who conducted the interviews, nor for the supervision of the survey, it is not immodest to say that the survey was well supervized, and the investigators were well trained and keen. There were eight investigators for 12 villages, each of which differed sharply from the other 11 (Chambers and Harriss 1977). Four investigators had only one village each, but the other four each had two villages. On the basis of the survey data, I wrote an article on agricultural extension, and intended to submit it for publication. But the more I looked at it, the more I sensed something was wrong. Eventually I took the results from the eight shared villages and paired them by investigator. The results from each village were more like those of its pair, shared by the same investigator, than like any other village. It seemed likely that the main independent variable was the investigator; and the basis for the article collapsed. By occurring in a well supervized survey, this experience throws into question the credibility of other surveys which do not test for and report on individual interviewer bias. Few do. And the fact that the literature on this bias is so sparse may reflect that even those who do carry out tests, sin as I did in holding back from publishing the damning findings.

More generally, critical discussion of methodological problems so rarely accompanies publications of survey results that the validity of the findings of much of the survey industry is open to question. For our purposes here, the conclusion is that the quality of data from questionnaire surveys is often so poor, that an improvement is not difficult to achieve.

This is, though, no reason for anything less than strict critical rigour in assessing the validity and reliability of RRA and PRA approaches and methods. The tests most readily applied concern measurements and numbers. Let us therefore examine the four main areas where RRA and PRA have generated numerical data which are available for assessment. These are farm and household surveys; wealth and wellbeing ranking; village censuses; and rainfall data.

8.1 FARM AND HOUSEHOLD SURVEYS

In five cases comparisons have been made between the findings of an RRA approach and a conventional questionnaire survey.

Michael Collinson's (1981) Exploratory Survey of a farming system involving some 20 professional person days was never contradicted in any major way by the subsequent longer-drawn out and more expensive Verification Survey which represented the major commitment of professional time and funds.

Steven Franzel and Eric Crawford (1987) systematically compared a quick and light survey with a longer and heavier conventional survey in Kenya and found no significant differences attributable to the methods.

Diane Rocheleau and her team (Rocheleau **et al.** 1989) working on agroforestry in Kenya used a chain of informal in-depth interviews, and group interviews, and compared the results with a survey of a formal randomized sample of 63 households. They found that 'the formal survey took three times as long and reproduced the same results as the group interviews and chain of interviews, with less detail and coherence' (**ibid**:21).

Andy Inglis (1990, 1991) led a team which used a repertoire of RRA techniques to gather local forestry knowledge in Sierra Leone in an area where a lengthy questionnaire with 278 questions had already been applied. The RRA results were presented four days after the last location was surveyed, but the questionnaire report was still not available six months after the completion of fieldwork. Comparisons of the questionnaire survey and RRA data showed sharp discrepancies in two localities where the questionnaire survey's findings were implausible and its validity had to be suspect. As Inglis points out:

> ..if information is wrong to begin with, no amount of statistical manipulation will enable it to help the project staff make good decisions....In contrast, the RRA survey was completed in a much shorter time, the results have been produced in specific locational reports that can be individually used as discussion papers in the field in follow up surveys. As research biases, mistakes and omissions are admitted and not lost in a mass of questionnaire codes, the decision maker can see how the information was generated, how important factors were revealed, and how the best bests were arrived at.'
>
> (Inglis 1990: 107)

C.N. Bernadas (1991) reports that in Eastern Visayas in the Philippines, highly structured questionnaire interviews identified declining soil fertility as the most pressing problem of farmers. Bernadas explains that 'The staff themselves had formulated the questions on the basis of what they felt to be priorities. The problem areas considered were predetermined based on the outsiders' point of view'. Two years of research based on the questionnaire survey findings did not match farmers needs and circumstances, and the developed technologies were not adopted by them. An RRA approach was then used, with informal discussions and dialogues and open-ended interviews with guide topics. This led to the discovery that the most pressing problem facing farmers was not soil fertility but the long fallow due to the growth of a weed **cogon (Imperata cylindrica)**. Relevant research could then begin.

In these five cases, then, the outcomes of the RRA approach, compared with the more formal questionnaire, were variously more valid, less costly, more timely, and more useful.

A cautionary counter example is a case of the worst of both worlds. This was a one-week survey through interviews of 30 farmers by a researcher in Northern Zambia, described as an RRA. Johan Pottier (1992) argues persuasively that in such hurried interviews an insensitivity to the context, to who is being met, to what is being said, and why, can lead to misleading conclusions, in this case that food security had been enhanced by growing maize. The investigation was, it seems, rushed and wrong. The lessons are many; and include that hectic one-off individual interviews are bad practice whatever the label attached to them, and that respondents can react by giving responses which, for reasons such as prudence, politenesses and favourable presentation of the self, are invalid but reliable, and thereby convincingly maintain myths and mislead.

8.2 RANKING

Ranking and scoring have long been part of the repertoire of social anthropologists. People in communities rank other individuals or households for characteristics as varied as aggressiveness, drunkenness, industriousness, or more commonly some concept of respect, honour, wellbeing or wealth (Pelto and Pelto 1978:82-87; *RRA Notes* 15, 1992).

The most common method is sorting cards into piles, carried out either by individuals in private, or by groups. Different informants often use different numbers of piles for the same community, but evidence is consistent in finding close correlations in rank orders between different informants. Sydel Silverman (1966:905) found that 'there was high agreement in the relative rank of most persons' when three informants in an Italian community card-sorted households according to their criterion of **rispetto** (approximately prestige). Polly Hill (1986:41,75) suggests that to villagers, relative household living standards can be a matter of passionate concern. On the basis of fieldwork in West Africa and India, she concluded that rural people (unless themselves too poor and disabled) are able to assess the relative wealth or wellbeing of members of their community far more accurately than are townspeople. This has been borne out by much subsequent wealth or wellbeing ranking. Barbara Grandin (1988) found that correlations (Spearman's Rho) across informants in 12 instances of wealth ranking (using a total of 41 informants) averaged .77 (range .59 - .96). The correlations of each informant with the final score averaged .91 (range .84 - .98).

Silverman, Hill and Grandin are all social anthropologists and so might be expected to have developed good rapport before the exercise. The test is whether without a social anthropological training and relationship, the method can also be reliable and valid. Those who have facilitated such ranking exercises have found them easier than expected (see *RRA Notes* 15) and informally report high correlations between the rankings given by different informants or groups. Some triangulate rankings through discussion. Polly Hill's three informants in Nigeria thrashed out discrepancies between themselves (Hill 1972:59). In a PRA mode, on similar lines, MYRADA in South India has evolved a method of successive approximation in which separate groups rank households, and then meet to reconcile differences (pers comm Vidya Ramachandran), a procedure which is used in selecting households for anti-poverty programmes.

Another example is the ranking of the value of 30 browse plants as feed to their cattle by pastoralists in Nigeria (Bayer 1987,1988). Rankings for the most important plants were found to correspond closely between different groups of pastoralists.

Not all ranking exercises can be expected to yield reliable and valid data; but these examples suggest close correlations between informants in three conditions: where information is common knowledge; where criteria are commonly held and well understood; and where what is ranked is a matter of intense interest.

8.3 PARTICIPATORY VILLAGE CENSUSES

In participatory social mapping, villagers show the location of households. In India in 1991 this was extended by Sheelu Francis and others into participatory censuses. One variant is health mapping, in which symbols are used to indicate where people of different types and with different conditions live in a village. In a census, one common practice is for villagers to use seeds of different sorts to represent people. Another, invented by Anusuda and Perumal Naicker of Kethanayakanpatty village near Madurai in Tamil Nadu, is to have a card for each household and mark details with symbols on the card.

Triangulation of censuses took place in Ramasamypatti village, near Tiruchuli, in Tamil Nadu, in May 1991. In a PRA training organized by SPEECH, an NGO, four groups of between five and 15 villagers used different methods of analysis and presentation: two did social mapping direct onto paper; one made a ground model of the village with a card for each household; and one did a seed census onto a map drawn on a floor. All four independently generated a figure for the total population of the village. All four came to 355.

8.4 RAINFALL DATA

It has been found that farmers will often readily estimate rainfall by month. In 1988 two farmers in Wollo in Ethiopia estimated numbers of days of rainfall by month for the previous five years, and also indicated the pattern they remembered from their childhood (Conway 1988; ERCS 1988:50-52). The most common method now is for them to arrange a line of 12 stones for the months of the local calendar and then estimate rainfall using either broken sticks for relative volume, or seeds for numbers of days of rain by month, or both. Some farmers in India have preferred to indicate depth of soil moisture by month as being more relevant for agricultural purposes (pers.comms. J. Mascarenhas for Karnataka and Sam Joseph for Rajasthan). A refinement, invented by women in Galkada village, Badulla District, Sri Lanka in January 1992, is to space the seeds to indicate the distribution of days of rain within each month.

The question is how valid such data are. Farmers' data on rainfall have several times been found to differ from those of nearby rainfall stations. At Nugu Dam in H.D.Kote, Karnataka, in August 1990, a discrepancy was found but not further analysed. In rapid catchment analysis in Kenya (Pretty 1990) when farmers' patterns of rainfall differed in six different catchments and also differed from the 'real' data from a nearby rainfall station, this was judged to reflect spatial heterogeneity, without ruling out the possibility that the farmers were wrong (pers. comm. J. Pretty). The only detailed analysis of comparisons to date comes from Nepal. It was there in May 1990 near Lumle that farmers for the first time indicated volume and numbers of days of rainfall per month using seeds for days and sticks for volume. In 45 minutes, they presented first a normal year and then a pattern which they said occurred one year in five. Gerard Gill's (1991) painstaking analysis of their perceptions compared with 20 years of daily rainfall data at the nearby rainfall station defies brief summary. Suffice it to say here that what initially appeared as discrepancies where the farmers were 'wrong' turned out on closer examination to show respects in which the farmers' judgements were superior to the averaged met station data. Gill's title 'But how does it compare with the **real** data?' captures the irony of the assumption that 'scientifically' measured data are necessarily superior. More balanced conclusions are that there are different realities, that farmers' realities are likely to be linked to agricultural utility and weighted by recent experience, and that the issue is whose reality counts, in what contexts, and for what purposes.

These four sets of numerical evidence are all positive for RRA/PRA approaches and methods. To the best of my knowledge and belief I have not excluded any comparable negative evidence. All the same, a terminal caveat is in order. When the four groups at Ramasamypatti all came up with 355 as the population of the village, I was excited. I collected the reporting maps and diagrams, labelled and arranged them, and then photographed them. This positive evidence has since been disseminated through copies of the slides. Only later did I think to ask whether there had been any exchanges of information or of figures between the groups. In fact I believe there was none. But had the groups come up with figures which differed, the question is whether my reaction too would have differed. The danger is selective recording and dissemination of the positive. Similarly with rainfall, the Nepal case has been meticulously analysed by Gill and published. But this was not done in the Kenya and Karnataka cases. Had those discrepancies been investigated further, they might, as in the Nepal case, have revealed a validity in the farmers' judgements; or they might not. We do not know with any certainty.

The lesson is at all times to keep critically aware, with a positive scepticism, and to probe, investigate, report and learn from negative as well as positive experience. With that caution, the finding from evidence available to date stands, that both qualitative and quantitative data elicited by RRA and especially PRA methods have usually proved more reliable and more valid that outsider professionals have expected.

As with all PRA, much depends on the behaviour and attitudes of the outsiders, and whether they have the time, patience and will to get closer to reality. A final example from Nepal illustrates a typical learning process through crosschecking and successive analysis and approximation. After the use of PRA methods, presentations by two groups of outsiders on what villagers had shared with them on seasonality and trends in agriculture gave conflicting information.

> The response was for both groups to go back to their village the next day and reconcile the information, with their respective groups of informants forming one combined group, and with the statement 'We got the information from you yesterday and there seems to be some difference. Can you help us?'And of course they did. Information flowed, arguments and discussions took place among the villagers, among the outsiders and between both villagers and outsiders - as is typical of a good PRA exercise. Explanations were given, corrections made, and it was a much more satisfied group of researchers that returned to the base camp that night.
>
> (pers. comm. James Mascarenhas)

Discrepancies are, as here, welcomed, in the spirit of embracing error, as opportunities to learn and to get closer to the truth.

9 REVERSALS AND REALITY

The power and utility of RRA and PRA are, then, empirical facts; and as such, they demand explanation.

Some explanations lie in the effective application of the principles outlined in section 5 above. But crosscutting these, there are other angles from which PRA experience can be examined and illuminated. So far, most of those who have innovated in developing PRA have been practitioners, concerned with what works, and what will work better, not academic theorists concerned with why it works. They have been searching not for new theories or principles but for new and better ways of learning and doing. The 'why?' questions have been relatively neglected. There is now, though, enough experience to allow us to induce some theory or explanations from practice.

The strongest explanations can be captured by the word 'reversals'. Reversal is used to describe a direction, away from normal practice and towards its opposite. The overarching reversal is from from etic to emic, from our knowledge, categories and values to theirs. It answers the question 'whose reality counts?' initially with the reply 'theirs'. We start with their reality, not with ours.

Within the frame of that reversal, three clusters of reversal or change intertwine, and are mutually reinforcing: reversals of modes; reversals of relationships; and reversals of action. None is absolute; but all represent shifts from the normal in the reverse direction.

9.1 REVERSALS OF MODES

a From closed to open

Conventional investigations are preset. Almost all questionnaire surveys are designed by outsiders with outsiders' concerns and categories. They seek to elicit responses to fill fixed boxes. Whatever the intentions that investigators shall probe under the category 'other' which lies at the end of the list of precoded responses on the sheet, they rarely do; and where they do it presents problems later in coding and analysis. The convenient truth fits our familiar frame.

The reversal here is from etic to emic, and from closed to open. In contrast with questionnaire interviews, semi-structured interviews are more open, and conversations even more so. There can be a checklist for reference, but not a preset sequence of questions. A value is set on probing, on pursuing leads, on serendipity. Moreover, with other methods common in PRA such as participatory mapping and modelling, matrix ranking and scoring, Venn or chapati diagramming and wellbeing ranking, insiders are not only free to express their knowledge and values; they are encouraged and enabled to do so. The shift is from preset to participatory.

b From individual to group

Questionnaire surveys require that interviews be with individuals or households so that commensurable data can be analysed. In RRA, semi-structured interviewing can be with an individual or group, but with somewhat more emphasis on the individual 'interviewee' (see e.g. Grandstaff and Grandstaff 1987b:135-7). In PRA, discussions with individuals can and do take place, but there is relatively more group activity. Cultural, social and other differences can be expected. Groups have well known disadvantages, such as dominance by one or more individuals. But on the positive side, especially in a PRA mode when rapport is good, they have strengths. Paradoxically, and contrary to common belief, sensitive subjects are sometimes more freely discussed in groups, when individuals would not wish to discuss them alone with a stranger. More generally, groups can build up collective and creative enthusiasm, especially with mapping and modelling, leading to an unselfconscious showing, sharing, and checking. Participants fill in gaps left by others and add or correct detail. Groups have an overlapping spread of knowledge which covers a wider field and crosschecks.

c From verbal to visual

With outsider-insider interactions, there is a scale of formality - informality, from the structured interview with questionnaire, through the semi-structured interview with checklist of subtopics (Grandstaff and Grandstaff 1987b), to the conversation (Scrimshaw and Hurtado 1987). With the interviews, and sometimes also conversations, outsiders ask questions and probe. Eye contact is common. The outsider maintains control, and largely determines the agenda and the categories. The interviewee responds, conscious of an interaction with a person who is seeking information. The transfer or exchange of information is verbal.

With PRA methods in contrast, much of the medium is visual, through forms of participatory diagramming. This includes social and census mapping, resource mapping and modelling, seasonal analysis, Venn and chapati diagramming, trend diagramming, and matrix ranking and scoring. The many forms of

The shift from verbal to visual is one of emphasis in PRA. Diagrams are part of the repertoire. They can be facilitated on their own early in interactions. They can also be part of semi-structured interviews or conversations, introduced as a means for local people to express, share and analyse their knowledge. Diagrams then present an agenda for discussion. 'Interviewing the map', 'interviewing the matrix', and 'interviewing the diagram' are often the most fruitful, and also most neglected, stages of a discussion and diagramming process. With the visual, 'a whole new set of questions and discussion arises which does not in the verbal' (pers. comm. James Mascarenhas). Combinations of visual and verbal, with early primacy to the visual, can be strong, and stronger than either exclusively on its own.

d From counting to comparing

Normal professional training is to make make absolute measurements. So if trends or changes are to be identified, or conditions compared between households or between places, this is through measurements made either at different times, or of different things, or in different places. Our preoccupation with numbers drives us to ask 'how much?' For sensitive subjects like income, such questions commonly sow suspicion, wreck rapport, and generate misleading data.

Often, though, all that is needed for practical purposes is relative values. Comparing can be quicker. Comparisons without measurements have advantages. Involving reflection and judgement, they are easier to express than measurements. They can be elicited for trends and changes without baseline data. They are less sensitive, as has been shown by wealth and wellbeing ranking, and by seasonal analysis: asking how income compares between months is both easier to judge and less worrying to give than are absolute figures. And comparisons, as with matrix ranking and scoring, can in a short time elicit a wealth of information and judgements of value inaccessible without great labour by other methods. Moreover, trends, comparisons and weightings lend themselves to visual sharing, with all its potential gains in participation, triangulation and progressive approximation and learning. Comparing can be quicker, cheaper and more credible than counting.

9.2 REVERSALS OF DOMINANCE: FROM EXTRACTING TO EMPOWERING

Both the traditional questionnaire survey, and the classical social anthropological investigation are extractive, even though their means of extraction differ.

In questionnaire interviewing, it is with the interviewer that power and initiative lie. The questionnaire is 'administered to' the person interviewed. The interviewee is a 'respondent', a person who replies or reacts. The Latin respondere means to return like with like. The questions and categories are those of the interviewer, who also records the 'response'. In their textbook, **Survey methods in Social Investigation,** Moser and Kalton have only, two entries for 'respondent', but 32 for 'response'. The professional concern is less with people - the respondents, and more with what they provide - the responses. It is the responses that matter more, for they are the raw material to be mined, packaged, transported and processed, the commensurable output to be collected, categorized, coded, counted and correlated.

The ultimate aim of the classical anthropologist too has been to obtain data which are then analysed and written up away from the field. Participant observation requires sharply different relationships to those in questionnaire surveys, but the basic aim is similar. There are of course qualifications to this. Development anthropologists aim to be useful through their work in a more direct manner; and many anthropologists intervene in their field for ethical reasons. But the motivation has usually been, and remains, that of a researcher. However useful and justified it may be, the consummation sought is to process the data extracted into a PhD, articles or a book.

In contrast, the thrust of PRA is to reverse who is dominant. The objective is less to gather data, and much more to start a process. The initiative is passed to 'them'. The stick is handed over. The prime actors are the people. The outsider is less extractor, and more convenor and catalyst.

A PRA process also seeks to enable outsiders to learn, but through the sharing of information in a manner which enhances people's analysis and knowledge and leaves them owning it. The actual and the ideal, here as elsewhere, will rarely correspond exactly. But an ideal could be sketched as a process in which people are enabled to collate, present and analyse information, making explicit and adding to what they already know. This happens, for example, through participatory mapping of a watershed where the map is used by villagers to plot current conditions and plan actions, and retained by them for monitoring action taken and changes; or through mapping and surveying degraded forest, deciding how to protect it and what to plant, and then managing the resource; or through matrix scoring for varieties of a crop which enables them to specify the characteristics of a 'wish' variety they would like to try out. The aim is to enable people to present, share, analyse and augment their knowledge as the start of a process. The ultimate output sought is enhanced knowledge and competence, an ability to make demands, and to sustain action. Instead of imposing and extracting, PRA seeks to empower.

9.3 FROM RESERVE TO RAPPORT, FROM TEDIUM TO FUN

The initial reserve of rural people towards outsiders, and their careful responses in the hope of gaining benefits or avoiding loss, are a commonplace. RRA and more so PRA stress the process of gaining rapport. Some social anthropologists have expressed scepticism about the relative speed with which rapport can be established. For their deeper and more fully emic understanding, there is a case for more lengthy immersion. But it is a common experience with both RRA and PRA that when the outsiders' behaviour and attitudes are right, and participatory methods used, good rapport usually comes quickly. This is through not rushing, through showing respect, through explaining who you are, answering questions, being honest, and being interested; and asking to be taught, being taught, and learning village tasks.

The classical view of fieldwork is that it is painful, entailing long hours of collecting and checking data. Moser and Kalton (1971:296) observe of questionnaire surveys 'An interviewer's interest is bound to flag after a time...'. Pelto and Pelto (1978; 1978: 194-5) cite the case of an anthropologist, Kobben, who had to make 'a great sacrifice of time, during a year of field work, to collect... quantified data on a mere 176 persons' and even then he felt rather unsure of the validity of some of his data. The same authors go on to consider how extensive survey data from questionnaires needs to be checked and qualified by other methods, and conclude:

> Clearly, the quantified data of survey research or other standardized interviewing require close support from participant observation and general informal interviewing. But the converse is equally true. The lesson in all this, as Kobben made clear, is that field research entails a great amount of tedious, time-consuming work - both qualitative and numerical.'
>
> (ibid: 194-5)

Earlier participatory research also suffered from being long-drawn-out. The pilot project in appropriate technology for grain storage in Bwakira Chini village in

Tanzania involved an outside team residing in the village for eight weeks. This was considered a 'short period of dialogue', but even so the application of the dialogical methodology was 'time consuming and tiresome' (Mduma 1973:203,213).

The contrast with RRA is sharp. Professional conversations are mutually stimulating and interesting. Of cattlekeepers in Nigeria who ranked browse plants, Wolfgang Bayer (1988:8) wrote that 'Pastoralists were very willing to share their knowledge about browse plants with us and appeared to enjoy the interviews as much as we did'. Reflecting on the comparison between a topic RRA and a questionnaire survey on forestry and fuelwood in Sierra Leone, Andy Inglis (1991:40) wrote that the RRA approach enabled respondents 'to enjoy a professional chat about their livelihood or kitchen habits, instead of being subjected to an intrusive 278 question questionnaire by bored enumerators.'

With PRA the contrast is even sharper. Data are not collected by outsiders, but presented by insiders. For outsiders, in John Devavaram's words (*RRA Notes* 13:10), 'One doesn't get bored repeating field work. It is always interesting'. What is shared is often unexpected and at times fascinating. For insiders, the creative act of presentation and analysis is usually a pleasure, and a process too of learning through the expression, sharing and augmenting of what they know. In matrix scoring for trees or varieties of a crop, using the ground and seeds, it is a common experience for the outsider to become redundant as the the process takes off, as villagers debate and score on their own. After village participants had made and analysed models ('maquettes') of their environment in Burkina Faso, 'tous les participants expriment le vif desir de continuer ce travail et de l'approfondir' (Hahn 1991:3). Quite often, dissatisfied with their first attempt at a map, villagers scrub it out and start again with concentrated enthusiasm. Again and again, villagers in India have lost themselves in mapping and modelling, and outsiders have had to learn not to interview, not to interrupt, not to disturb their creativity. There is pride in what has been made, and pleasure in presenting it to others. So often PRA is fun.

10 EXPLAINING OUR PAST IGNORANCE

There remains a puzzle why it has taken until the 1990s for all this to come together; for the confluence of streams (Section 1) to occur; for the principles (Section 4) to begin to emerge; for the menu to methods to reach its present richness (Section 5); for the practical applications to be made (Section 7); for the degree of validity and reliability of RRA and PRA to become evident (Section 8); for the power of reversals of mode and dominance to be recognized (Section 9); and for the potentials for empowerment, fascination and even fun to be expressed as they have. At a personal level, I am bemused to understand how for several decades I have been working in rural development without knowing about all this. More generally, it is a mystery why it has taken so long for the development community as a whole to 'discover' the richness not just of the knowledge, but of the creativity and analytical abilities of villagers.

Some of the mystery disappears if we look for explanation in ourselves. The beliefs, behaviour and attitudes of most outsiders have been the same all over the world. Agricultural scientists, medical staff, teachers, officials, extension agents and others have believed that their knowledge was superior and that the knowledge of farmers and rural people was inferior; and that we, the professional outsiders, had a monopoly of powers of analysis. Most outsiders have then either lectured, holding sticks and wagging fingers, or have interviewed, machine-gunning with rapid fire questions, interrupting, and not listening beyond immediate replies. We have 'put down' rural people. Our reality has blanketed theirs. Our beliefs, demeanour, behaviour and attitudes have then been self-validating. Treated as incapable, rural people have behaved as incapable, hiding their capabilties from us, and even from themselves. Nor have we known how to enable them to express, share and extend their knowledge. The ignorance and inabilities of rural people have been not only an illusion, but an artifact of our own arrogance and ignorance.

For participatory approaches and methods to take off, a stage had also to be reached when different conditions could come together: recognition of past error and inadequacy, as with agricultural research for resource-poor farmers; greater confidence and professionalism in rural NGOs; approaches like agroecosystem analysis which simply did not exist before the 1980s; and finally, the emergence of an international community of communication with a critical mass and momentum in which approaches and methods could be shared between disciplines, countries, and organizations, as at IDS in 1979, Khon Kaen in 1985 (KKU 1987), and Bangalore in 1991 (Mascarenhas et al. 1991). Perhaps then it is understandable that these new participatory approaches and methods, in their many forms and with their many labels, are now clustering and coalescing more, as philosophy, approaches, repertoire and practice. Their time may have come.

11 DANGERS

Any such up-beat statement must at once be qualified. For RRA and PRA five dangers stand out.

The first danger is **faddism**. Like farming systems research, RRA and PRA could be discredited by over-rapid adoption and misuse, and by sticking on labels without substance. The warning signs are there: demand for training which exceeds by far the tiny cadre of competent trainers; requirements that consultants 'use RRA' or now 'use PRA' and then consultants who say they will do so, when they do not know what RRA or PRA entail or are the wrong sort of people to be able to do them well; and the belief that good RRA or PRA are simple and easy, quick fixes, when they are not.

The second danger is **rushing**. The word 'rapid', necessary in the late 1970s and early 1980s, is now a liability. It has been used to legitimize brash and biased rural development tourism. Much of the rationale for RRA/PRA has been to make time to find the poorest, to learn from them, and to empower them. Hurry and lack of commitment compound errors, and mean that the poorest are, once again, neither seen, listened to, nor learnt from. The R of RRA stands better for 'relaxed', allowing plenty of time.

The third danger is **formalism**. In the long term, this may prove the most difficult. With any innovation, there is an urge to standardize and codify, often in the name of quality. Manuals are called for and composed. They can indeed be useful as compilations of experience, as cookbooks that widen the choice of recipes, as sources of ideas, especially for trainers. But manuals can also harm. With any new approach or method, manuals start short but grow fast. Paragraphs proliferate as intelligent authors seek to cater for every condition and contingency. Some farming systems research gave rise to manuals the weight and volume of which was itself a problem. (For example, the four volumes of Farming Systems Support Project Manuals (FSSP 1987) weigh, on our kitchen scales, approximately 3.6 kg). The dangers are evident. Training is based on the text, and takes longer. More time is spent in the classroom teaching the theory and less in the field learning the practice. Spontaneity is inhibited and spread slowed, stopped or reversed.

The initial lack of a manual for PRA in India has then been an advantage. Would-be practitioners have been forced to learn, not from books, and not by rote, but from colleagues, through sharing, and from their own improvizations and experiences in the field. Many of the best innovations have happened when practitioners have not known or followed whatever rules there were. Matrix scoring came about when someone broke the rules for matrix ranking. The first guidelines for wealth ranking (Grandin 1988) presented individual interviews in private as the preferred method, but many practitioners have now found ways of using group interviews; by mid-1991, MYRADA had conducted over two hundred wealth rankings by groups (pers. comm. Vidya Ramachandran). Nor has the criterion for ranking remained some concept of 'wealth'. More commonly now, more complex and diverse concepts of wellbeing, as defined by rural people themselves, are used.

The largest and heaviest manual in India in mid-1992 is that produced by Ravi Jayakaran of Krishi Gram Vikas Kendra. The reader opens it to find printed boldly on the first page:

USE YOUR OWN BEST JUDGEMENT AT ALL TIMES

The other pages are all blank.

The lesson is that practitioners must take responsibility for what they do. They must feel free to start, to make mistakes, and to learn on the run. It is not books of instructions, but personal commitment, critical awareness, and informed improvization, which can best assure quality and creativity.

A linked, fourth, danger is **ruts**. Practitioners and trainers fall into habits and routines. There are many different ways of doing participatory mapping and modelling, transects, walks, seasonal analysis, group interviews, ranking and scoring, identifying special groups of people, and the like. But practitioners in any organization, or even region, show signs of slipping into unvarying standard practices, overlooking other options. Of course, some routinization and repetition are inevitable, even desirable. But experimenting, inventing, testing, adapting and constantly trying to improve are part of the potential strength of PRA. To nurture and keep that spirit, one means is exchanges of trainers between organizations, countries and continents, to share approaches, methods and experiences in the field.

A final danger or difficulty is **rejection**. Some of the many pioneers who contributed to the streams - participatory research, participatory action research, applied anthropology, agroecosystem analysis, farming systems research, and RRA itself - which have fed into PRA may feel that they have not received due recognition, when what they should really feel is pleasure and pride; and others, especially academics, may feel excluded, bypassed or threatened, by the developments described in this paper, and so reject them. At worst this will mean that students in colleges and universities, and staff in field organizations, are denied access to and the opportunity to use PRA approaches and methods. At best, it will mean a positive contribution through constructive criticism which will sharpen the rigour and add to the repertoire of PRA. It can only be hoped that the spirit of sharing will encourage and allow all professionals to own, use and develop PRA approaches and methods. For it is the monopoly of no person or group. As it grows, PRA is, and should remain, an open access resource.

12 FRONTIERS, CHALLENGES AND POTENTIALS

The future presents many frontiers, challenges and potentials. Eight stand out.

12.1 BEYOND FARMING SYSTEMS RESEARCH (FSR)

Farming systems research faces problems because of the diversity, complexity and uncontrollability of many farming systems, especially rainfed farming in the South. Participatory approaches known variously as farmer-back-to-farmer (Rhoades and Booth 1982), farmer participatory research (Farrington and Martin 1988) and farmer first (Chambers, Pacey and Thrupp 1989) have moved towards involving farmers to undertake their own analysis. This is potentially parsimonious in the use of scientists' time (Chambers and Jiggins 1986) but its methods are still in an early stage of development.

Pioneering work by many of those working in India, and by Jacqueline Ashby of CIAT, Clive Lightfoot of ICLARM, Jules Pretty of IIED, and others has shown that farmers have diagramming and analytical capabilities which were not hitherto suspected. In India and Malawi, Lightfoot and others have facilitated ground diagramming by farmers of nutrient flows on their farms, and elsewhere, diagramming of their farming systems by farmers. Anil Shah of AKRSP, in March 1991, facilitated the diagramming on paper by a farmer, Savasi Bhura, of Gadhechi Village, Surendranagar District, Gujarat, of a complex flow and causal diagram of the impact of irrigation. Jules Pretty, in Pakistan in early 1992 found during a training exercise that non-literate as well as literate farmers could make detailed diagrams of flows and causality on their farms, including an impressive diagram by a non-literate woman. Elsewhere in 1992, in India and Botswana, matrix scoring for varieties of a crop has been developed by asking analysts to add a 'wish' variety in which farmers specify the characteristics they would like extension and scientists to provide for them.

The challenge now is for outsider professionals to further develop and disseminate approaches and methods to help farmers do their own analysis and make their own needs and priorities known to scientists. If such efforts continue to be successful, the implications for activities, procedures, training, rewards and institutional cultures in agricultural education, research and extension will be little short of revolutionary.

12.2 POLICY RESEARCH AND CHANGE

At a policy level RRA/PRA have recently begun to be a strong source of insights. Examples from Zimbabwe, Tanzania, Chad and Nepal illustrate the potential.

In Zimbabwe in November 1991, RRA with PRA methods was used to investigate the effects on agriculture of structural adjustment policies. RRAs were conducted by a team of researchers over two weeks in two Communal Areas. Their findings and recommendations, in a report (FSRU 1991) completed straight after the fieldwork, provided immediate feedback from the field concerning marketing, transport, input supply, prices, food security, and farmers' attitudes towards agricultural structural adjustment policies, and provided policy makers with insight into the farmers' eye view and their intentions.

In Chad, in 1991 a survey was undertaken on a national scale using RRA techniques to try and understand how people perceived their food security problems, and what solutions they proposed (Buchanan-Smith 1992). Thirteen survey enumerators worked in 55 representative villages, spending about a day in each village. A group interview with a checklist as guide was followed by household interviews, particularly oriented towards women (who were rarely represented in the group interview). Three years of different weather conditions were used as reference points. Organizing and analysing the mass of data was achieved despite difficulties, and lessons were learnt for improving this sort of survey. Three categories of administrative areas were found, each with a distinctive household food security strategy. The results challenged the conventional thinking in N'djamena which held that the key to raising production was promoting free market systems for agricultural produce. The survey showed that local people knew methods and technologies to increase production but were constrained by lack of credit for ploughs, oxen, improved seeds, and more efficient irrigation, and that more was needed than developing agricultural marketing alone.

Another striking example is provided by land policy in Tanzania (Johansson and Hoben 1992). As a contribution to a Government reassessment of land policies, the Institute of Resource Assessment at the University of Dar es Salaam organized four RRAs for mid-level policy-makers. Four villages were chosen to represent a range of conditions. Four teams were formed, and each spent five days in one of the villages. Through the direct learning of the RRAs they concluded that the Government's top-down approach was wrong, that communities and people were already doing land use planning, that imposing a land use map was misguided, and that new participatory approaches were needed. They presented their findings to a seminar with high-level policy makers. The resulting recommendations from the seminar entailed major reversals of policy, and seemed 'to indicate just how great an impression such a short visit to a rural area can have and how effective an RRA can be in providing relevant insights for policy makers and planners' (**ibid.** 30).

These three examples were one-off efforts. A prototype for a more permanent facility is being tested in Nepal. There, eight small Rapid Deployment Teams have been trained in basic PRA methods and are in place at different locations in the terai (lowland). The intention is that they will simultaneously use PRA methods to investigate and report on aspects of policy and conditions, providing comparative insight for policy-makers (pers. comm. Gerard Gill). A similar approach, but without PRA methods and without teams, was developed with ten representative villages in Sri Lanka in the mid-1970s (Senaratne 1976) but was not sustained. If the Nepal initiative is effective, it could represent a breakthrough for wide application in other countries.

The potential here appears vast. So often the State is self-deceiving through misleading information fed back through official channels (Chambers forthcoming).

Perhaps in contrast policy-makers could now, through improved RRA and PRA approaches and methods have available information and insights which are more immediately up-to-date, reliable and credible.

12.3 PERSONAL BEHAVIOUR, ATTITUDES AND LEARNING

All too often senior officials, scientists and academics who pronounce and prescribe on rural development lack recent direct knowledge, and base their analysis and action on ignorance or on personal experience which is decades out of date. Top-down, centre-outwards, prescription in the name of science and modernity is alive and well, even in the 1990s.

It is not a new idea that rural development would gain if senior officials and policy-makers were able to spend time unofficially living and learning in rural conditions, but little appears to have been done. An exception is the Exposure and Dialogue Programme of the German Commission of Justice and Peace which for some years has been enabling senior outsiders to learn the life stories of village people (Kochendörfer-Lucius and Osner 1991; Osner et al. 1992). In a less structured manner, senior officials in India have appreciated the opportunities to spend time incognito in villages, with their interactions unconstrained by official protocol. At a personal level, the methods of PRA offer new scope, and make mini-sabbaticals easier to envisage. PRA approaches and methods provide ways in which officials, scientists and academics can come face-to-face with rural people in an informal and non-threatening mode which both sides can find rewarding. They can also provide experience and learning which are intellectually exciting, practically relevant, and often enjoyable.

Behaviour and attitudes can, though, be an impediment, sometimes irremediable. A senior government officer, an able scientist, a distinguished academic, an experienced NGO worker, a local-level extensionist or health worker - any of these, depending on personality, experience and circumstances, can either take to PRA with enthusiasm or reject it with passion. Much needs to be learn about how in the rural context to facilitate changes in outsiders' behaviour and attitudes.

Some methods have already been devised, such as Anil Shah's 'shoulder tapping'. He has written that, taking District Officers in Gujarat on a transect walk to see the problems of soil erosion

'I told them in advance that a transect in Participatory Rural Appraisal (PRA) is for observation and to understand the knowledge and perception of the farmers. We do not advise, but ask - ask open-ended questions without implied advice. I told them that this was very difficult for educated people, more so for those in authority. Therefore, when I heard anyone giving advice or asking questions with implicit advice, I would tap his shoulder and if necessary offer my services to rephrase the advice or query into an open-ended question.'

By the end of half a day, and several taps, a lot had been learnt that would otherwise have been missed (Shah 1992). More such methods, and much more experience with them, are needed.

The policy and personal potentials of RRA/PRA interlock. Their scope has scarcely begun to be tapped. The frontier here is to see how to scale up, how to enable many more policy-makers at all levels, as well as others at the local level, personally to gain direct learning experience in the field from and with rural people, enabling them to fit policy and action more to local conditions and priorities and to the needs of the poor.

12.4 SPREAD WITH QUALITY ASSURANCE

In strategic discussions about RRA and PRA quality has been a recurrent concern. The term quality control has given way to quality assurance, since no person or organization can exercise control. Increasingly, the conclusion has been that assurance has to be personal, and that quality depends on the individual practitioner.

One dilemma here is how far to encourage would-be practitioners and trainers to start on their own. The danger is that bad performance will lead to discredit and disillusion. The opportunity is for wider and faster spread. A problem is that capability depends on personality. Some people have a facility for using the 'right' language, especially at international conferences, but behave in the 'wrong' manner in the field, dominating, lecturing, interfering, interrupting, and holding on to the stick. One solution may be for more shared field experience, for trainers to conduct training together, for more mutual 'shoulder tapping', and more learning from each other.

Appendix A, 'Start, stumble, self-correct, share' is an attempt to encourage launching out and trying PRA approaches and methods, and learning by doing. Nothing in rural development is ever a panacea; and PRA faces problems of spread, scale and quality assurance. The potential realized will depend largely on practitioners and trainers. The questions are whether critical self-awareness, embracing error, using one's own best judgement at all times, and constantly trying to do better can be built into the very genes of PRA; and if so, whether RRA and PRA can be not just self-spreading, but self-improving.

12.5 EMPOWERMENT AND EQUITY

Good PRA empowers. Those who, through PRA, express and share what they already know, learn through that expression and sharing. Those who investigate and observe add to their knowledge. Those who analyse become yet more aware and reach new understanding. Those who plan and then implement what they have planned take command, and further learn through the experience of action.

Whether empowerment is good depends on who are empowered, and how their new power is used. If those who gain are outsiders who exploit, or a local elite who dominate, the poor and disadvantaged may be worse off. Whether PRA is equitable and good, depends then on whom it involves. The 'natural' tendency is for this to be men rather than women, the better off rather than the worse off, and those of higher status groups rather than those of lower status. The challenge is then so to introduce and use PRA that the weaker are identified and empowered and equity is served.

Fortunately, tools available suit this task. Sequences such as participatory mapping, household listing, wellbeing ranking, and livelihood analysis can identify groups distinguished according to local values. Focus group discussions can then identify the priorities and interests of different categories of people, including, or especially, those who are disadvantaged. The contrasts can be sharp. Drawing on applications of PRA techniques in Sierra Leone, Ghana, Malawi and Bangladesh, Alice Welbourn (1991) has shown how significant can be differences of ethnic group, age, gender and economic status, and combinations of these. With pastoralists in Kenya, Jeremy Swift and Abdi Noor Umar (1991:56) found marked and striking differences of priority: out of a possible maximum of 100, livestock management was scored 87 by the rich, but only 7 by the poor, and lack of livestock 0 by the rich but 49 by the poor.

Differentiating groups and interests can empower the poorer in several ways. It can give them collective awareness and confidence to confront others and argue their case: Youth for Action, an NGO based in South India, has worked at first in some villages only with Harijans (Untouchables) so that they gained in confidence and capability before later the rest of the village was involved. AKRSP(India) convenes groups of women and men separately to choose the numbers of trees of different sorts they want in their nursery, and then helps them reconcile their differences. Differentiation through wealth or wellbeing ranking can help an outside organization select and deselect those with whom it will work: ActionAid and MYRADA, both in South India, have used PRA methods to identify the poorer who then gain more from their programmes.

PRA methods such as diagramming can also be brought into play to clarify and resolve conflicts. Agroecosystem diagramming was used in the Philippines to make explicit the differences of interests between groups after the construction of a small dam at Lake Buhi and to achieve consensus about priorities (Conway, Sajise and Knowland 1989; Conway 1989). In the approach of the Neighbourhood Initiatives Foundation in the UK, a large model of a neighbourhood allows people to address conflicts by putting down suggestions, and using markers to agree or disagree without needing to identify themselves. This 'depersonalises conflicts and introduces informality where consensus is more easily reached'(Gibson 1991).

The identification, expression and resolution of conflicts of interest remains a frontier for participatory methods. The next few years will show what potential there is. The worst is that participatory methods may so enhance the awareness of the disadvantaged and encourage their organization and action that a backlash is provoked which leaves them weaker and worse off. One hope can be that diagrams can be used to defuse tension by focussing public debate. They can make differences permanently explicit, and can direct discussion to a visible thing rather than to individual people.

To explore this frontier demands sensitive commitment, and time. PRA methods to identify differences of interest and priority are well known. Methods for negotiation and equitable conflict resolution are less so. It is perhaps in this domain as much as any other that there is need and scope for new participatory methods.

12.6 SUBSTITUTING FOR SURVEYS

Rural questionnaire surveys are one of the largest rural industries. They are also one of the most protected and inefficient. They have hitherto not been subjected to a market challenge. Like Henry Ford's Model T automobile, mass produced, durable, and all the same colour, they are routinely turned out in a standard form. In the case of some repetitive national surveys, like the National Sample Survey in India, there may be no full substitute. But other, **ad hoc**, surveys are continuously being commissioned. Administering questionnaires is still the normal mode of rural research. Indeed, for many academics and others, even now in the early 1990s, rural research **is** questionnaire surveys.

Donors and governments alike have maintained demand for questionnaire surveys through their concern with monitoring and evaluation (M&E). Funds are set aside for baseline surveys so that later progress can be monitored and projects evaluated. Few such baseline surveys have ever been useful, let alone worth the resources invested in them. The reasons include difficulties in ensuring comparability in subsequent surveys, in assessing the counterfactual (what would have happened without the project), in finding comparable controls, and in identifying causality.

It is too early to say that the days of the standard questionnaire survey are numbered. Like the Model T it is robust and durable, the public is fond of it, and it employs many workers who lack other skills. Some managers (academics, consultants) like it because it keeps them off the shop floor (out of the field). But the market for the Model T declined as better and more varied alternatives were developed, and with large questionnaire surveys, there are similar straws in the wind, if not yet writing on the wall: the National Council of Applied Economic Research, probably the largest survey organization in India apart from the National Sample Survey, has been trying out rapid and participatory methods as an alternative or complement to questionnaire surveys, and with positive results; a leading PRA practitioner and trainer, Sam Joseph, of ActionAid, Bangalore, when challenged, was able to specify a more cost-effective PRA method for obtaining all the items of data in a standard baseline survey; and as noted above eight teams of researchers in Nepal, trained in PRA methods, are attempting to generate simultaneous and comparable insights from different locations.

To take but one method, participatory mapping has proved powerful as part of an alternative. Selina Adjebeng-Asem of Obafemi Awolowo University, Ife-Ife, Nigeria, has reported (pers. comm. July 1992) on its application in monitoring a soyabean project:

I trained the....Soyabean project group in the use of PRA for monitoring of the project impact in 5 states of the Federation i.e. Kaduna, Niger, Enugu, Anambra and Oyo States of Nigeria. The group of 16 researchers were amazed about how much easier it is to obtain indepth information through participatory mapping in addition to other RRA techniques they have already known. We were able through mapping to obtain all relevant socio-demographic information we required for the project; for example, the number of households in a village, households involved in soyabean production, gender issues in soyabean production, utilization of soyabean, and preference rankings of various soyabean diets.......We gathered an incredible amount of information within an hour and a half visit to the village....The researchers have been begging me to give more training in PRA...

In cases such as this, PRA methods, used well, can be not only more cost-effective than questionnaire surveys; they are also more popular with all concerned, researchers and rural people alike.

The use of PRA methods in M&E, and in research, raises issues of comparability and causality. Comparability of information shared in different contexts may become a big question in the 1990s. Decentralized and democratic processes may generate disparate data which central planners cannot then easily add up or compare. More remains to be learnt about how and how well PRA methods can generate commensurable data (for example demographic, health and agricultural information) from different places; and to what extent central planners and officials can tolerate and manage incommensurability, and variability in the form of locally shared information and locally generated plans.

With causality, PRA methods have advantages over questionnaire surveys. Statistical correlations and regressions do not establish causality. People who live in an area have a comparative advantage in knowing and interpreting what has happened there, and PRA now has relevant tools to help them conduct their own analysis.

The need now is to multiply and assess more tests, experiments and innovations, like those of the NCAER in India, of Winrock in Nepal, and of Adjebeng-Asem in Nigeria, in order to learn how far rapid, relaxed and participatory approaches and methods can substitute for, and improve upon, questionnaire surveys.

12.7 SPREAD BY VILLAGERS

A finding of the PRA experience has been (see 6.1. above) that rural people can do much that outsiders have thought they could not do. One by one the dominoes have fallen as they have shown that they can map, model, rank, score, estimate, diagram and analyze more and better than expected. Often, too, they can do this better than outsiders. The working rule has become to assume that people are capable of something until it is proved otherwise.

One frontier then becomes the development and spread of PRA and related approaches and methods by villagers themselves. Extension has in recent decades been thought of as an activity for the field staff of Government organizations or of NGOs, usually with high recurrent costs. The question is whether, and if so how, to 'hand over the stick' to farmers and villagers themselves, and whether this can be sustainable through local demand for the service provided.

Farmers' own extension has a long history, probably as old as farming itself. Deliberate training of farmers as extensionists may be more recent. As one example, in the 1980s in Central America, World Neighbours trained volunteer extensionists and gradually handed over responsibilities for experiments and extension to them (Bunch 1985). In India, both MYRADA and SPEECH have invited villagers who had already gained experience of PRA to take part as facilitators of training in other villages.

The Aga Khan Rural Support Programme (India) has taken this further. In the late 1980s, it developed village volunteers as an approach in which villagers were trained as facilitators both for their own and for other villages. The village volunteers were not just to be extensionists, but to facilitate the PRA approach and methods (Shah 1989; Shah, Bharadwaj and Ambastha 1991). The village volunteers came to provide services for which people were prepared to pay, not only from their own but from other villages. They also were enabled to form teams to conduct PRA exercises in other villages. 'These teams are doing these exercises in a number of villages involving mapping, transect diagramming, interviewing, group discussions, prioritization and preparation of a village natural resources management plan. It is observed that they enjoy the process...' (Shah **et al.** 1991:87-88). In February 1992, a team of village volunteers demonstrated their skills as facilitators to an international group of visitors in Kabripathar village, Bharuch District, Gujarat. In one day, the village volunteers enabled villagers to map their degraded forest, count and measure rootstock in five quadrats on the ground, assess numbers of nursery plants needed, and through matrix scoring, analyse needs and choose numbers of each species (M. Shah, forthcoming). In July 1992 it was reported that village volunteers conducting PRAs had told AKRSP staff that now 'they need not bother to attend'.

The question now is whether spread through village volunteers can become self-sustaining and self-improving. The incentive systems evolved by AKRSP and villagers involve payment by results, rewarding good performance. Demand exists from new villages for the services of village volunteers. It remains to be seen whether village volunteers on their own will be able and willing to train village volunteers in new villages, who will then in turn be in demand. Were that to occur, and with market incentives for good performance, what began as a programme initiated from outside, might become self-spreading. Were that not to occur, it might still be feasible for organizations like AKRSP to foster spread with a light touch, training volunteers and encouraging them to form teams that sell their services.

12.8 PRA IN INSTITUTIONS

Perhaps the biggest challenge is the establishment of PRA as a way of operating, even as a culture, in organizations. Normal bureaucratic tendencies to standardize, centralize, and impose top-down targets at best impede and at worst prevent the open-endedness, flexibility, creativity and diversity of much good PRA. To establish PRA as the norm in an organization therefore requires reversals and a change of culture.

Three main types of organization have been involved: NGOs; Government field organizations; and universities and training institutes.

Those organizations which have embraced and developed PRA have shared three characteristics. The leadership has been stable and committed to PRA; a substantial proportion of staff have personally wished to use PRA approaches and methods; and there has been recurrent training and reinforcement. Commitment of a director or principal of an institution is on its own not enough; nor, on its own, is repeated training. Nor does it seem useful to train at lower field levels without higher level commitment. It is critical that the middle-level managerial staff in any organization genuinely, and not just verbally, wish to use or support PRA. If they do not, there are innumerable small ways in which their lack of support can undermine and finally eliminate PRA initiatives.

Not surprisingly, much of the initial innovation and spread has been among NGOs, since their organizational cultures quite often share values with PRA. Some, like IIED based in the UK, and MYRADA and AKRSP in India, have undertaken training for Government field organizations, and have defined or begun to redefine their roles to include PRA training for others. Adoption and use in Government field organizations is more problematical (see Section 7 above). To learn more from experience already gained with strategy and tactics is a priority that will be addressed in a forthcoming issue of *RRA Notes*.

In the long term, universities and training institutes are strategically vital. Currently, many of them disable those who pass through them, conditioning them with attitudes and behaviour of superiority, and teaching methods which then have to be unlearnt. Rehabilitation can then be tiresome, painful, costly, and far from always successful.

Globally, RRA and PRA have to date still made little impression in universities and training institutes. The scale of adoption of RRA and PRA remains minuscule compared with the scope. The potential for applications in training and education remains vast and almost entirely unrecognized. Only when many more universities and other tertiary institutions for education and training introduce RRA and PRA into their curricula, teaching and fieldwork, and when a new generation of professionals is well versed in their principles and methods, and the behaviour and attitudes which go with them, will its acceptance and spread become truly wide.

To this absence in universities, four exceptions can be noted regionally.

First, in Southeast Asia, several universities in Thailand (notably the pioneering University of Khon Kaen) and the Philippines (including the University of the Philippines, Los Banos) have been using RRA for years. A comparative study is overdue to understand why and how they came to adopt it, and their experience in legitimating, teaching and further developing it.

Second, among universities in sub-Saharan Africa, those with practitioners of RRA and PRA include Egerton University in Kenya (with a link with Clark University, Worcester, Mass, USA), Obafemi Awolowo University, Ife-Ife, Nigeria, and the University of Zimbabwe, Harare.

Third, in the early 1990s, some key training institutions in India and Nepal started to adopt and develop the PRA approach and methods. These include the National Academy of Administration at Mussoorie, the Indian Institute of Forest Management at Bhopal, and the Xavier Institute of Social Service at Ranchi, and the Institute of Forest Management at Pokhara in Nepal. All these are believed to be using PRA methods in the village fieldwork of their students in place of questionnaire surveys. At the same time, a number of Agricultural Universities in India, including the Narendra Dev University of Agriculture and Technology, Faizabad and other Eastern Indian Agricultural Universities, the Tamil Nadu Agricultural University, and the Hebbal Agricultural University, Bangalore, have invited lectures, workshops and training in PRA and related methodologies.

Fourth, staff in several Australian Universities have taken up and practised RRA and PRA. Historically, this followed a paradigm shift in agricultural education, to systems thinking and self-directed learning, in Hawkesbury Agricultural College (now the University of Western Sydney) in the early 1980s (Bawden et al 1984; Dunn 1991). University faculties and schools some of whose staff have been involved in RRA and PRA include the Faculty of Agricultural and Rural Development, University of Western Sydney, Hawkesbury; the School of Crop Sciences at the University of Sydney (Ampt and Ison 1989; Ison n.d.); the School of Agriculture at Charles Sturt University, Riverina (Dunn and McMillan 1991); and the Law School, Macquarie University (Voyce et al. 1989). One RRA in Australia identified intra and inter generational conflict and the transfer of the family farm as neglected topics of concern to many farmers (Ampt 1988; Ampt and Ison 1988; Ison 1990) and then RRA techniques were used to study the transfer of the family farm (Voyce et al 1989). RRA has also been used for the identification of grassland research problems (Ampt and Ison 1989). In September 1991 participants from several institutions combined as a team to facilitate a PRA in the Kyeamba Valley which enabled landholders and their families to identify and analyse issues of concern, and to plan action (PRA Team 1991).

Pathways of dissemination are not easy to foresee, but this Australian example may be a pointer. With this form of global sharing, the normal direction of transfer of innovation is reversed, and approaches and methods evolved in developing countries are adopted and adapted in rich countries.

13 THE PARADIGMATIC SIGNIFICANCE OF PRA

One contribution to be sought from universities is a better understanding of underlying theory. In Australia, RRA has been linked with soft systems theory (Checkland 1981) and contextual science (Russell and Ison 1991). In making these links, Australian researchers have begun to explore further the paradigmatic significance of RRA and PRA.

The word 'paradigm' is used with various meanings. Here I shall use it to mean a coherent and mutually supporting pattern of concepts, values, methods and action, amenable to wide application.

In his paper (Jamieson 1987) 'The paradigmatic significance of RRA', delivered at the International Conference on Rapid Rural Appraisal at Khon Kaen in 1985, Neil Jamieson argued that RRA, with its rapid learning, fitted and supported a new and emerging paradigm of development. Despite ideological conflicts, Marxists, socialists and capitalists had shared evolutionary, unilineal, universalistic, positivistic and utilitarian assumptions, and a fervent belief in progress. Another view of development, he said, was of human evolution as problem-solving under pressure, as adaptive change. This fitted better with a cybernetic systems approach, which included the concepts of feedback, of lead time (the time between receipt of information and when it is too late to use it), and of lag time (the time between receipt of information and the completion of action based on it)(see also Joseph 1991). Jamieson argued that change had accelerated and unpredictability had increased, making accurate and timely feedback more than ever vital for effective adaptive change.

Much that Jamieson wrote not only still applies, but applies now with more force than in 1985. At a theoretical level, chaos theory has shown more clearly how patterns and directions of change can be sensitive to small differences in starting conditions (Gleick 1987). At the empirical level, changes in local and global conditions - ecological, social and political - appear to be accelerating. In conditions of faster and faster change, and of increasing unpredictability, it matters more even than before to have timely feedback, prompt learning and rapid adaptive responses.

Perhaps more significantly, parallel shifts of paradigm are now occurring in three domains: in science; in business management; and in development itself.

In **science**, conventional approaches, using hard systems and reductionist assumptions and methods, are in crisis when faced with many of our important problems (Mearns 1991; Appleyard 1992). Scientific method is not competent to predict or prescribe for the complex open systems which matter most. Global environmental issues involve huge uncertainties and demand what Funtowicz and Ravetz (1990) call a 'second order science' in which judgement plays a more recognized part. Precise understanding, prediction and prescription for local agro-eco-social systems can be similarly elusive. This is not a new discovery. Jeremy Swift wrote in 1981:

> ..a major World Bank livestock development project in Mali is based, for crucial calculations of sustainable grazing pressure, on the report of a highly competent ecologist in 1972; the calculations were redone in 1977/78 by a different, equally well-qualified ecologist, who halved the earlier carrying capacity. Nobody is to blame; the science is inexact. But the consequences could be disastrous for the project, and more so for the pastoralists involved.
>
> (Swift 1981: 487)

Perhaps no one was to blame then. But now we know more about what is not knowable using the standard methods of 'disciplines'. When so much is so unknowable and so unpredictable, solutions have to be sought through methodological pluralism, through flexible and continuous learning and adaptation, and through the exercise of judgement.

In **business management**, the parallel shift has been from the values and strategies of mass production to those of flexible specialization (see e.g. Kaplinsky 1991: 7). Standardization has been replaced by variety and rapid response, hierarchical supervision by trust, and punitive quality control by personal quality assurance at source. Much in Tom Peters' book of advice to American business managers, *Thriving on Chaos: Handbook for a Management Revolution* (1987), applies equally in PRA. He advocates, for example, 'achieving flexibility by empowering people', 'learning to love change', becoming obsessed with listening, deferring to the front line, and 'building systems for a world turned upside down'. A highly successful Brazilian manager, when he took over a company, abolished norms, manuals, rules and regulations, and put the company's employees 'in the demanding position of using their own judgement' (Semler 1989: 79). It has been the discipline of the market and opportunities from new technology which have driven and drawn business management to decentralized flexibility, to diversification, and to finding and exploiting transient niche markets. For PRA and related approaches, the discipline is what works with people and communities, and the opportunities of the new approaches and methods, which drive and draw. In both business management and PRA, value is placed on decentralization, sharing knowledge, empowerment, diversity, and rapid change and feedback. So it is that the philosophy and approaches of PRA can be seen as one expression of a wider paradigm for effective action in the contemporary world.

In **development**, theories of universal economic growth as the main means to a better life are less credible than ever (see e.g. Ekins 1992, Sachs 1992 **passim**). As economic growth ceases to be a simple, universal objective, as it is recognized as environmentally harmful among the richer, and as economic resources are recognized as finite, so it matters more to enhance the quality of life through other more sustainable means. For the rich, the question is how to be better off with less; for the poor, it is how to gain more and be better off with what they can gain, but without repeating the errors of the rich. These objectives can be served by enabling local people to identify, express and achieve more of their own priorities. In line with this, the emergent paradigm for human living on and with the earth brings together decentralization, democracy and diversity. What is local, and what is different, is valued. In this paradigm, the trends towards centralization, authoritarianism, and homogenization are reversed. Reductionism, linear thinking, and standard solutions give way to an inclusive holism, open systems thinking, and diverse options and actions.

RRA and more so PRA are, then, part of a more general paradigm shift. They resonate with and support methodological pluralism, rapid adaptive change, the analysis and expression of local people's priorities, and democratic local diversity. Like future 'development', the future of PRA is unknowable; but the promise is there. How much of that promise is realized, how soon, and how well, will be determined by professionals in NGOs, Government services, training and research institutes, and universities. Closed or open, conservative or radical, reductionist or pluralist, timid or bold, as guardians of the old or as inventors of the new, they will determine this through personal choice.

ABBREVIATIONS AND ADDRESSES

ActionAid	ActionAid, 2 Resthouse Road, Postbox 5406, Bangalore 560001, India
AKRSP	Aga Khan Rural Support Programme (India), Choice Premises, Swastik Cross Roads, Navrangpura, Ahmedabad 380 009, India
IDS	Institute of Development Studies, University of Sussex, Brighton BN1 9RE, UK
IIED	Sustainable Agriculture Programme, International Institute for Environment and Development, 3 Endsleigh Street, London WC1H ODD, UK
MYRADA	MYRADA, 2 Service Road, Domlur Layout, Bangalore 560 071, India
NCAER	National Council for Applied Economic Research, 11 I.P. Estate, New Delhi 110002, India
NIF	Neighbourhood Initiatives Foundation, Chapel House, 7 Gravel Leasowes, Lightmoor, Telford TF4 3QL, UK
ODI	Overseas Development Institute, Regent's College, Inner Circle, Regent's Park, London NW1 4NS
PRA	Participatory rural appraisal
RRA	Rapid rural appraisal
SPEECH	14 Jeyaraja Illam, Kiruba Nagar, Madurai 625 014, India

REFERENCES

ActionAid, 1991, **Jamkhed: Participatory Rural Appraisal in Identifying Major Illness, Healthcare Providers and Costs,** ActionAid, Bangalore

Ampt, P.R., 1988, 'Rapid Rural Appraisal' Forbes Shire, February 1988 **Initial Report,** School of Crop Sciences, University of Sydney

Ampt, P.R. and Ison, R.L., 1988, 'Report of a Rapid Rural Appraisal to idntify problems and opportunities for agronomic research and development in the Forbes Shire, NSW' School of Crop Sciences, University of Sidney, December

____ 1989, 'Rapid Rural Appraisal for the identification of grassland research problems', **Proceedings of the XVI International Grassland Congress,** Nice, France, pp 1291-2

Appleton, Judith, 1992, 'Notes from a food and nutrition PRA in a Guinean fishing village', **RRA Notes** 16 pp 77-85

Appleyard, B., 1992 **Understanding the Present: Science and the Soul of Modern Man,** Picador, published by Pan Books, London

Ashby, J.A., 1990, **Evaluating Technology with Farmers: a Handbook,** IPRA Projects, Centro Internacional de Agricultura Tropical (CIAT), AA 6713, Cali, Colombia, December

Bawden, R.J., Macadam, R.D., Packham, R.J. and Valentine, I., 1984, 'Systems thinking and practice in agricultural education', **Agricultural Systems** 13, pp 205-225

Bayer, W., 1987, 'Browse quality and availability in a farming area and a grazing reserve in the Nigerian subhumid zone', Report to the ILCA Subhumid Zone Programme, Kaduna, Nigeria, Gottingen, May

Bayer, W., 1988, 'Ranking of browse species by cattlekeepers in Nigeria', **RRA Notes** 3 pp 4-10, December

Beebe, J., 1987, 'Rapid Appraisal: The evolution of the concept and the definition of issues', in **KKU Proceedings** pp 47-68

Belshaw, D., 1981, 'A theoretical framework for data-economising appraisal procedures with applications for rural development planning', in R. Longhurst (ed.) **IDS Bulletin** Vol 12 No 4, pp 12-22

Bentley, Margaret E., Pelto, Gretel H., Straus, Walter L., Schumann, Debra A., Adegbola, Catherine, de la Pena, Emanuela, Oni, Gbolahan A., Brown, Kenneth H. and Huffman, Sandra L., 1988, 'Rapid ethnographic assessment: applications in a diarrhoea management program', **Social Science in Medicine** Vol 27 No 1, pp 107-116

Bernadas, C.N., Jr., 1991, 'Lesson in upland farmer participation: the case of enriched fallow technology in Jaro, Leyte, Philippines', **Forests, Trees and People Newsletter** 14, October, pp 10-11

Biggs, S., 1980, 'Informal R & D', **Ceres**, Vol 13 No 4, pp 23-26

BRAC, 1983, **The Net: Power Structure in Ten Villages**, Bangladesh Rural Advancement Committee, 66 Mokhahali Commercial Area, Dhaka 12

Bradley, Sarah Murray, 1992, 'Visual literacy: a review with an annotated bibliography', mimeo, IIED, London

Brokensha, David W., Warren, D.M. and Werner, O. 1980, **Indigenous Knowledge Systems and Development**, University Press of America, Lanham, Maryland

Buchanan-Smith, M., 1992, 'Finding out how people prioritize their food security problems in Chad: the challenges of RRA at national level', mimeo, IDS, Sussex

Bunch, R., 1985, **Two Ears of Corn: A Guide to People-Centered Agricultural Improvement**, World Neighbors, 5116 North Portland, Oklahoma City, Oklahoma 73112

Campbell, G. J., Shrestha, R. and Stone, L., 1979, **The Use and Misuse of Social Science Research in Nepal**, Research Centre for Nepal and Asian Studies, Tribhuvan University, Kirtipur, Kathmandu

Carruthers, Ian and Chambers, Robert, 1981, 'Rapid Appraisal for rural development', **Agricultural Administration** Vol 8 No 6, pp 407-422

Case, D'Arcy Davis, 1990, **The Community's Toolbox: The Idea, Methods and Tools for Participatory Assessment, Monitoring and Evaluation in Community Forestry**, Community Forestry Field Manual 2, FAO, Rome

Cernea, Michael (ed.), 1985, **Putting People First: Sociological Variables in Development Projects**, The Johns Hopkins Press, Baltimore

Chambers, Robert, 1981, 'Rapid Rural Appraisal: rationale and repertoire' **IDS Discussion Paper** No 155, IDS, Sussex

____ 1992, 'The self-deceiving state', **IDS Bulletin**, Vol 23 No 4 IDS, Sussex

Chambers, Robert and Harriss, John, 1977, 'Comparing twelve South Indian villages: in search of practical theory', in B.H. Farmer (ed.) **Green Revolution? Technology and Change in Rice Growing Areas of Tamil Nadu and Sri Lanka**, pp 301-322

Chambers, Robert and Jiggins, Janice, 1986, 'Agricultural research with resource-poor farmers: a parsimonious paradigm' **IDS Discussion Paper** 220, IDS, Sussex

Chambers, Robert, Pacey, Arnold and Thrupp, Lori Ann, (eds.), 1989, **Farmer First: Farmer Innovation and Agricultural Research**, Intermediate Technology Publications, London

Checkland, P.B., 1981, **Systems Thinking, Systems Practice**, John Wiley, Chichester

Collinson, M., 1981, 'A low cost approach to understanding small farmers', **Agricultural Administration**, Vol 8 No 6, pp 433-450

Convergence, 1975, Vol 7 No 2, 1981, Vol 14 No 2, and 1988, Vol 21 Nos 2 and 3: special issues on participatory research

Conway, G., 1985, 'Agroecosystem analysis', **Agricultural Administration**, 20 pp 31-55

____ 1986, **Agroecosystem Analysis for Research and Development**, Winrock International Institute for Agricultural Development, PO Box 1172, Nana Post Office, Bangkok 10112

____ 1987, 'Rapid Rural Appraisal and agroecosystem analysis: a case study from Northern Pakistan', in **KKU Proceedings** pp 228-254

____ 1988, 'Rainbow over Wollo', **New Scientist** 5 May

____ 1989, 'Diagrams for farmers', in R. Chambers, A. Pacey and L.A. Thrupp (eds.) **Farmer First**, pp 77-86

Conway, G., Sajise, P. and Knowland, W., 1989, 'Lake Buhi: resolving conflicts in a Philippines development project', **Ambio** Vol 18 No 2, pp 128-135

Cornwall, Andrea, 1992, 'Body mapping in health RRA/PRA', **RRA Notes** 16 pp 69-76

Cresswell, Teresa, 1992, 'Unemployment and health: the development of the use of PRA in identified communities in Staveley, North Derbyshire', **RRA Notes** 16 pp 27-30

Daane, J.R.V., 1987, 'Quelle Méthode pour l'Analyse de Systèmes de Production en Zone Rurale Tropicale: Le Dilemme entre Démarche Quantitative Peu Fiable et Démarche Qualitative Peu Généralisable', contribution au 8ème Séminaire d'Economie Rurale, CIRAD, Montpellier

Devavaram, John, Nalini, J. Vimalnathan, Abdul Sarkar, Krishnan, A.P. Mayandi and Karunanidhi, 1991, 'PRA for Rural Resource Management', **RRA Notes** 13 pp 102-111

Dunn, A.M., 1991, 'New challenges for extensionists: targeting complex problems and issues', paper for the 10th European Seminar on Extension Education, Universidade de Tras-os-Montese Alto Douro, Vila Real, Portugal, September

Dunn, Tony and McMillan, Allan, 1991, 'Action research: the application of Rapid Rural Appraisal to learn about issues of concern in landcare areas near Wagga Wagga, NSW', paper presented to a Conference on Agriculture, Education and Information Transfer, Murrumbigee College of Agriculture, NSW, September 30 to October 2 1991

ECRS, 1988, **Rapid Rural Appraisal: a Closer Look at Rural Life in Wollo**, Ethiopian Red Cross Society, Addis Ababa and the IIED, London

Ekins, P., Hillman, Mayer and Hutchinson, Robert, 1992, **Wealth Beyond Measure: an Atlas of New Economics**, Gaia Books, London

Farmer, B.H., 1977, **Green Revolution? Technology and Change in Rice-Growing Areas of Tamil Nadu and Sri Lanka**, Macmillan, London and Basingstoke

Farrington, John, (ed.), 1988, **Experimental Agriculture**, Vol 24 Part 3

Farrington, John and Martin, Adrienne, 1988, 'Farmer participation in agricultural research: a review of concepts and practices', **Agricultural Administration** Occasional Paper No 9, ODI, London

Francis, Sheelu, Devavaram, John and Erksine, Arunothayam, 1991, 'Workshop on Participatory Rural Appraisal for Planning Health Projects', October 2-5 1991, **SPEECH**, Madurai

Francis, Sheelu, Devavaram, John and Erskine, Arunothayam, 1992, 'Training workshop on participatory rural appraisl for planning health projects', **RRA Notes** 16 pp 37-47

Franzel, Steven and Crawford, Eric, 1987, 'Comparing formal and informal survey techniques for farming systems research: a case study from Kenya', **Agricultural Administration** 27, pp 13-33

Freire, Paulo, 1968, **Pedagogy of the Oppressed**, The Seabury Press, New York

FSRU, 1991, 'Structural adjustment and communal area agriculture in Zimbabwe: case studies from Mangwende and Chivi communal areas: a report of a rapid rural appraisal exercise', Farming systems Research Unit, Department of Research and Specialist Services, Ministry of Lands, Agriculture and Rural Settlement, Harare, Zimbabwe, November

FSSP, 1987, **Diagnosis, Design and Analysis in Farming Systems Research and Extension**, Volumes I, II and III, and **Trainer's Manual**, Farming Systems Support Project, Institute of Food and Agricultural Sciences, University of Florida, Gainesville, Florida 32611, December

Funtowicz, S.O., and Ravetz, J.R., 1990, **Global Environmental Issues and the Emergence of Second Order Science**, Commission of the European Communities, Luxembourg

Gaventa, John and Lewis, Helen, 1991, 'Participatory education and grassroots development: the case of rural appalachia, **Gatekeeper Series** 25, IIED, London

Gibbs, Christopher, 1987, 'Rapid Rural Appraisal: an overview of concepts and applications', in **KKU Proceedings** pp 193-206

Gibson, Tony, 1991, 'Planning for real: the approach of the Neighbourhood Initiatives Foundation in the UK', **RRA Notes** 11 pp 29-30

Gilbert, E.H., Norman, D.W. and Winch, F.E., 1980, 'Farming Systems Research: a critical appraisal', **MSU Rural Development Paper** No 6, Department of Agricultural Economics, Michigan State University, East Lansing, Michigan 48824

Gill, G., 1991, 'But how does it compare with the real data?', **RRA Notes** 14 pp 5-14 (also **Research Report Series** Number 16, HMG Ministry of Agriculture-Winrock International, Kathmandu, January 1992)

____ forthcoming, 'Participatory methods in policy analysis for natural resource management', in **Natural Resource Economics of India: a Guidebook for Researchers and Policy Makers,** Oxford and IBH, New Delhi

Gleick, J., 1987, **Chaos: Making a New Science,** Heinemann, London

Gould, P., and White, R., 1974, **Mental Maps,** Penguin Books, Harmondsworth, UK

Grandin, Barbara, 1988, **Wealth Ranking in Smallholder Communities: a Field Manual,** Intermediate Technology Publications, 103 Southampton Row, London

Grandstaff, Terry B., and Grandstaff, Somluckrat W., 1987a, 'A conceptual basis for methodological development in Rapid Rural Appraisal', in **KKU Proceedings** pp 69-88

____ 1987b, 'Semi-structured interviewing by multidisciplinary teams in RRA', in **KKU Proceedings** pp 129-143

Grandstaff, Somluckrat W., Grandstaff, Terry B. and Lovelace, George W., 1987, 'Summary report', in **KKU Proceedings** pp 3-30

Groenfeldt, D., 1989, 'Guidelines for rapid assessment of minor irrigation systems in Sri Lanka, **Working Paper** No 14, International Irrigation Management Institute, Sri Lanka

Gueye, Bara and Schoonmaker, Freudenberger, Karen, 1990, **Introduction a la Methode Acceleree de Recherche Participative (MARP),** Centre de Recherches pour le Developpement International, BP 2435, Dakar, Senegal, Octobre

Gueye, Bara and Karen Schoonmaker Freudenberger, 1991, **Methode Acceleree de Recherche Participative,** IIED, London, August

Guijt, Irene, and Manneh, Karafa, Martin, Mary and Sarch, Terri, 1992, 'Reflections on the training: process and prospects', in **From Input to Impact: Participatory Rural Appraisal for ActionAid The Gambia**, ActionAid, The Gambia and IIED, London, March pp 1-19

Guijt, Irene and Pretty, Jules N., forthcoming, **Participatory Rural Appraisal for Farmer Participatory Research in Punjab, Pakistan**, IIED, London

Gypmantasiri et al. and Conway, Gordon, 1980, **An Interdisciplinary Perspective of Cropping Systems in the Chiang Mai Valley: Key Questions for Research**, Multiple Cropping Project, Faculty of Agriculture, University of Chiang Mai, Thailand, June

Hahn, H., 1991, **Apprendre avec les yeux, s'exprimer avec les mains: des paysans se forment à la gestion du terroir**, AGRECOL, Oekozentrum, CH-4438 Langenbruck, Switzerland

Harwood, R., 1979, **Small Farm Development: Understanding and Improving Farming Systems in the Humid Tropics**, Westview Press, Boulder, Colorado

Hill, Polly, 1972, **Rural Hausa: a Village and a Setting**, Cambridge University Press, Cambridge

IDS, 1979, 'Whose knowledge counts?', **IDS Bulletin** Vol 10 No 2

____ 1992, Some Sources on Rapid and Participatory Rural Appraisal

Inglis, Andrew Stewart, 1990, 'Harvesting local forestry knowledge: a field test and evaluation of rapid rural appraisal techniques for social forestry project analysis, dissertation presented for the degree of Master of Science, University of Edinburgh

____ 1991, 'Harvesting local forestry knowledge: a comparison of RRA and conventional surveys', **RRA Notes** 12 pp 32-40

Ison, Raymond I., (1990), 'Rapid Rural Appraisal: a participatory "problem" identification method relevant to Australian agriculture', School of Crop Sciences, University of Sydney 2006

Jamieson, N., 1987, 'The paradigmatic significance of RRA', in **KKU Proceedings** pp 89-102

Jayakaran, Ravi, 1991, 'PRA Camp at Mahilong, Bihar, 27-30 November 1990: Krishi Gram Vikas Kendra', **RRA Notes** 13 pp 118-122

Johansson, Lars, and Hoben, Allan, 1992, 'RRA's for land policy formulation in Tanzania', **Forests, Trees and People Newsletter** 14/15, February pp 26-31

Joseph, S., 1991, 'Lead time, lag time: RRA/PRA in ActionAid', ActionAid Postbox 5406, 2 Resthouse Road, Bangalore 560001

____ 1992, 'Participatory Rural Appraisal in identifying major illness, healthcare providers and costs', **RRA Notes** 16 pp 53-56

Joseph, Thomas, and Joseph, Sam, 1991, 'PRA in Malda District, West Bengal: report of a training workshop for ActionAid India and Tagore Society for Rural Development', **RRA Notes** 13 pp 95-101

Kabutha, Charity, and Ford, Richard, 1988, 'Using RRA to formulate a village resources management plan, Mbusanyi, Kenya', **RRA Notes** 2, October, pp 4-11

Kaplinsky, R., 1991, 'From mass production to flexible specialization: a case study from a semi-industrialized economy, **IDS Discussion Paper** 295, IDS, Sussex, November

Kassam, Yusuf, and Mustafa, Kemal, (eds), 1982, **Participatory Research: An Emerging Alternative Methodology in Social Science Research**, Society for Participatory Research in Asia, 45 Sainik Farm, Khanpur, New Delhi 110 062

KKU, 1987, **Proceedings of the 1985 International Conference on Rapid Rural Appraisal**, Rural Systems Research and Farming Systems Research Projects, University of Khon Kaen, Thailand

Kochendörfer-Lucius, G., and K. Osner, 1991, **Development Has Got a Face: Lifestories of Thirteen Women in Bangladesh on People's Economy**, Results of the International Exposure and Dialogue Programme of the German Commission of Justice and Peace and Grameen Bank in Bangladesh, October 14-22, 1989, Gerechtigkeit und Frieden Series, Deutsche Kommission Justitia et Pax, Kaiserstrasse 163, D-5300 Bonn 1

Kumar, Alok, 1992, 'Trends in health care', **RRA Notes** 16 pp 48-52

Kumar, Somesh, 1991, 'Anantapur experiment in PRA training', **RRA Notes** 13 pp 112-117

Lightfoot, Clive, **et al.**, 1991, **Training Resource Book for Participatory Experimental Design**, Narendra Dev University of Agriculture and Technology, Faizabad, UP, India; International Center for Living Aquatic Resources Management, Manila, Philippines; International Rice Research Institute, Manila, Philippines

Longhurst, R. (ed.), 1981, **Rapid Rural Appraisal, IDS Bulletin**, Vol 12 No 4

Lovelace, George W., Subhadhira, Sukaesinee and Simaraks, Suchint (eds.), 1988, **Rapid Rural Appraisal in Northeast Thailand: Case Studies**, KKU-Ford Rural Systems Research Project, Khon Kaen University, Khon Kaen, Thailand

McCracken, J. A., 1988, **Participatory Rapid Rural Appraisal in Gujarat: a Trial Model for the Aga Khan Rural Support Programme (India)**, IIED, London, November

____ 1990, 'BOBP tries out RRA in Chinnamedu, Tamil Nadu', **Bay of Bengal News**, June 1990 pp 2-5

McCracken, J. A., Pretty, Jules N. and Conway, Gordon R., 1988, **An Introduction to Rapid Rural Appraisal for Agricultural Development**, IIED, London

Mascarenhas, J., 1990, 'Transects in PRA', **PALM Series** IV E, MYRADA, 2 Service Road, Domlur Layout, Bangalore 560 071

Mascarenhas, J., and P.D. Prem Kumar, 1991, 'Participatory mapping and modelling: user's notes', **RRA Notes** 12 pp 9-20

Mascarenhas, J., **et al.**, 1991, **Participatory Rural Appraisal: Proceedings of the February 1991 Bangalore PRA Trainers Workshop, RRA Notes** Number 13, IIED, London and MYRADA, Bangalore, August

Maxwell, Simon, 1989, 'Rapid food security assessment: a pilot exercise in Sudan', **RRA Notes** 5

Mduma, E.K., 1982, 'Appropriate technology for grain storage at Bwakira Chini Village', in Kassam and Mustafa (eds.), **Participatory Research**, pp 198-213

Mearns, R., 1991, 'Environmental implications of structural adjustment: reflections on scientific method, **IDS Discussion Paper** 284, IDS, Sussex, February

Mearns, Robin, Shombodon, D., Narangerel, G., Turul, U., Enkhamgalan, A., Myagmarzhav, B., Bayanjargal, A. and Bekhsuren, B., 1992, 'Direct and indirect uses of wealth ranking in Mongolia', **RRA Notes** 15 pp 29-38

Moris, Jon R., 1970, 'Multi-subject farm surveys reconsidered: some methodological lessons, paper for the East African Agricultural Economics Society Conference, Dar es Salaam, 31 March to 4 April, 1970

Moser, C.A., and Kalton, G ., 1971, **Survey Methods in Social Investigation**, Second Edition, Heinemann Educational Books Ltd, London

Mukherjee, Neela, 1992, 'Villagers' perceptions of rural poverty through the mapping methods of PRA', **RRA Notes** 15 pp 21-26

NES, 1990, **Participatory Rural Appraisal Handbook**, National Environment Secretariat, Kenya; Clark University; Egerton University; and the Center for International Development and Environment of the World Resources Institute, February

Norman, D. W., 1975, 'Rationalizing mixed cropping under indigenous conditions: the example of Northern Nigeria', **Samaru Research Bulletin** 232, Institute for Agricultural Research, Samaru, Ahmadu Bello University, Zaria, Nigeria (also **Journal of Development Studies** n.d. pp 3-21)

Osner, Karl, Kochendörfer-Lucius, Gudrun, Müller-Glodde, Ulrike, and Warning, Claudia, 1992, **Exposure-und Dialogprogramme: Eine Handreichnung für Teilnehmer und Organisatoren**, Justitia et Pax, Kaiserstrasse 163, 5300 Bonn 1

Palm Series 1-5, MYRADA, 2 Service Road, Domlur Layout, Bangalore 560 071

Pelto, Pertti J., and Pelto, Gretel H., 1978, **Anthropological Research: the Structure of Inquiry**, second edition, Cambridge University Press

Peters, Tom, 1987, **Thriving on Chaos: Handbook for a Management Revolution**, Alfred A. Knople, USA

PID and NES, 1989, **An Introduction to Participatory Rural Appraisal for Rural Resources Management**, Program for International Development, Clark University, Worcester, Mass and National Environment Secretariat, Ministry of Environment and Natural Resources, Nairobi, November

Potten, D., 1985, 'Rapid Rural Appraisal - emergence of a methodology and its application to irrigation: a bibliographical review', paper for the Review and Development Seminar on Selected Issues in Irrigation Management, International Irrigtation Management Institute, Sri Lanka

Pottier, Johan, 1992, 'Agrarian change at the household level: investigative styles in research on Mambwe agriculture' in Preben Kaarsholm (ed.), **Institutions, Culture and Change at Local Community Level**, International Development Studies Occasional Paper 3, Roskilde University Centre, Denmark, pp 61-74

PRA Team, 1991, **The Kyeamba Valley: Issues of Concern to Landholders and Their Families, identified in a Participatory Rural Appraisal by Members of the Kyeamba Valley Community, September 1991**, compiled by a PRA Team with the following connections: Landcare, Department of Conservation and Land Management, New South Wales Agriculture, School of Agriculture,

CSU-R, Centre for Conservation Farming, CSU-R, School of Crop Sciences, The University of Sydney and Wagga Wagga City Council

Pretty, Jules N., 1990, **Rapid Catchment Analysis for Extension Agents: Notes on the 1990 Kericho Training Workshop for the Ministry of Agriculture, Kenya,** Sustainable Agriculture Programme, IIED, London, November

Pretty, Jules, Subramanian, S., Ananthakrishnan, D., Jayanthi, C., Muralikrishnasamy, S. and Renganayaki, K., 1992, 'Finding the poorest in a Tamil Nadu Village: a sequence of mapping and wealth ranking', **RRA Notes** 15 pp 39-42

Rahman, Md Anisur (ed.), 1984, **Grassroots Participation and Self-reliance,** Oxford and IBH, New Delhi

Ramachandran, Vidya, 1990, **A Workshop on Participatory Learning Methods, 8th to 12th January 1990, MYRADA Talavadi Project,** PRA/PALM Series No 1, MYRADA, Bangalore

Rhoades, Robert, 1982, **The Art of the Informal Agricultural Survey,** International Potato Center, Apartado 5969, Lima

____ 1990, 'The coming revolution in methods for rural development research', User's Perspective Network (UPWARD), International Potato Center (CIP), PO Box 933, Manila

Rhoades, R.E., and Booth, R., 1982, 'Farmer-back-to-farmer: a model for generating acceptable agricultural technology', **Agricultural Administration,** Vol 11 pp 127-137

Richards, P., 1985, **Indigenous Agricultural Revolution,** Hutchinson, London and Westview Press, Colorado

Rocheleau, Diane, Wachira, Kamoji, Malaret, Luis and Muchiri Wanjohi, Bernard, 1989, 'Local knowledge for agroforestry and native plants', in R. Chambers, A. Pacey and L.R. Thrupp (eds.) **Farmer First,** pp 14-24

RRA Notes 1-16 and continuing, Sustainable Agriculture Programme, International Institute for Environment and Development, 3 Endsleigh Street, London WC1H ODD.

Russell, David B., and Ison, Raymond L., 1991, The research-development relationship in rangelands: an opportunity for contextual science, **Plenary Paper for Fourth International Rangelands Congress**, Montpellier, France, 22-26 April

SPR in Asia, 1982, **Participatory Research: an Introduction**, Society for Participatory Research in Asia, 45 Sainik Farm, Khanpur, New Delhi 110062

Sachs, Wolfgang (ed.), 1992, **The Development Dictionary: a Guide to Knowledge as Power**, Zed Books, London and New Jersey

Scoones, I., 1988, 'Learning about wealth: an example from Zimbabwe', **RRA Notes** No 2

Scrimshaw, S., and Hurtado, E., 1987, **Rapid Assessment Procedures for Nutrition and Primary Health Care: Anthropological Approaches for Improving Programme Effectiveness**, United Nations University, Tokyo; UNICEF/UN Children's Fund; and UCLA Latin American Center, Los Angeles

Semler, R., 1989, 'Managing without managers', **Harvard Business Review**, September-October, pp 76-84

Senaratne, S.P.F., 1976, 'A program of micro-level studies in rural Sri Lanka' mimeo, no source given, 12 pages

Shah, Anil C., 1991, 'Shoulder tapping: a technique of training in participatory rural appraisal', **Forests, Trees and People Newsletter** 14, October, pp 14-15

Shah, Meera, forthcoming, 'Participatory afforestation programme: sequence adopted by Aga Khan Rural Support Programme (India)'

Shah, Parmesh, 1989, 'Concept of people's participation in the watershed development - extension volunteer approach', mimeo, AKRSP, June

____ 1990, 'Economic classification of a community using locally generated criteria' **RRA Notes** No 8

____ 1991, Sequences in Participatory Rural Appraisal (PRA): Background Note for the 24 October 1991 Joint IIED/IDS Workshop, IDS

Shah, Parmesh, Bharadwaj, Girish, and Ambastha, Ranjit, 1991, 'Farmers as analysts and facilitators in participatory rural appraisal and planning', **RRA Notes** 13 pp 84-94

Shaner, W.W., Philipp, P.F, and Schmehl, W.R., 1982, **Farming Systems Research and Development: Guidelines for Developing Countries,** Westview Press, Boulder, Colorado

Silverman, Sydel F., 1966, 'An ethnographic approach to social stratification: prestige in a central Italian community', **American Anthropologist** Vol 68 No 4: 899-921 (quoted in Pelto and Pelto 1978: 82-4)

Swift, J., 1981, 'Rapid Appraisal and cost-effective research in West Africa', **Agricultural Administration** 8, 6 November pp 485-492

Swift, Jeremy and Umar, Abdi Noor, 1991, **Participatory Pastoral Development in Isiolo District: socio-economic research in the Isiolo Livestock Development Project,** Isiolo Livestock Development Project, EMI ASAL Programme, Isiolo, Kenya

van Steijn, T., 1991, 'Rapid Rural Appraisal in the Philippines: report of a study on the application of RRA by Philippines NGOs, GOs and University Institutes', draft version for comment, Council for People's Development, 175B Kamias Road, Quezon City, Metro Manila, Philippines, July

Theis, J., and Grady, H., 1991, **Participatory Rapid Appraisal for Community Development: a Training Manual Based on Experiences in the Middle East and North Africa,** Save the Children and IIED, London

Tolley, Elizabeth and Bentley, Margaret E., 1992, 'Participatory methods for research on women's reproductive health', **RRA Notes** 16 pp 63-68

Voyce, M., **et al.**, 1989, 'The transfer of the family farm', **National Farmer** (Australia), 10 March, 1989 pp 1-17

Welbourn, A., 1991, 'RRA and the analysis of difference', **RRA Notes** 14 pp 14-23, December

____ 1992, 'A note on the use of disease problem ranking with relation to socio-economic well-being: an example from Sierra Leone', **RRA Notes** 16 pp 86-87

Whyte, A.V.T., 1977, **Guidelines for Field Studies in Environmental Perception**, UNESCO, Paris

Whyte, William Foote (ed.), 1991, **Participatory Action Research**, Sage Publications, Newbury Park, London, New Delhi

Wignaraja, Ponna, Akmal Hussain, Harsh Sethi and Ganeshan Wignaraja, 1991, **Participatory Development: Learning from South Asia**, United Nations University Press, Tokyo and Oxford University Press, Karachi

APPENDIX A

SOURCES OF INFORMATION

RRA Notes are a major source on PRA. **RRA Notes** 13 is recommended to any reader seeking a good introduction. **RRA Notes** are free on request from The Sustainable Agriculture Programme at IIED, 3 Endsleigh Street, London, WC1H 0DD.

The interest in **RRA Notes** is growing fast, and the series will continue to be sent out to those on the mailing list. The complete set of back issues is costly, and means the occasional reprinting of back copies. IIED have therefore started a system of charging for back copies as follows:

1 In future, IIED will send out up to two back copies free of charge.

2 For requests for more than 2 copies, IIED will charge £2.50 per issue. This includes the costs incurred for reprinting and for postage.

3 For a full set of 15 back copies the charge will be £33.00.

For information about field experience, training opportunities and national PRA networks contact:

In Australia: A M Dunn
School of Agriculture
Charles Sturt University, Riverina
PO Box 588, Wagga Wagga, NSW 2650
tel: 61-69-222385; fax: 61-69-222812

In Bangladesh: Aroma Goon
PACT
House 56, Road 16 (New) 27 (old)
Dhanmondi R/A, Dhaka 1209
tel: 880-2-324091/815953; fax: 880-2-813416

In Botswana: S. Nkhori
Production Systems Programme
Department of Agricultural Research
P.O.Box 10, Mahalapye
tel: 267-410677

In India: Sam Joseph
ActionAid
3 Resthouse Road, Bangalore 560 001
tel: 91-812-586682/586583; fax: 91-812-586284
telex: 845 2142 AAIN IN

In Indonesia:

Mary Ann Kingsley
World Education
Jalan Tebet Dalam IV F/75
Jakarta 12810
tel: 62-21-829-1026; fax: 62-21-850-5440

In Kenya:

Elkanah Odembo Absalom
World Neighbours
PO Box 14728, Nairobi
tel: 254-2-440614; fax: 254-2-443443
telex: 25413 NORFU KEN

In Nepal:

Gerard Gill
Winrock International
PO Box 1312, Kathmandu
tel: 977-1-212987/222904; fax: 977-1-222300
telex: 2305 APROSC NP

In Nigeria:

Oluwayomi David Atte
Department of Geography, University of Iloren
Iloren
tel: 234-31-221552-5; fax: 234-31-223170

In Norway:

John Jones
Centre for Partnership in Development
PO Box 23, Vinderen, 0319 Oslo 3
tel: 47-22-451818; fax: 47-22-451810

In Pakistan

Richard Edwards
ActionAid
House 5, St. 32, F8/1 Islamabad
tel: 92-51-858126; fax: 92-51-851821

In Senegal:

Bara Gueye
ENEA, BP 5579, Dakar
tel: 221-253176
(Can also be contacted via IIED - see under UK contact)

In South Africa: Tessa Cousins
Association for Rural Advancement
PO Box 2517, Pietermaritzburg 3200
fax: 27-331-455106

In Sri Lanka: Mallika Samaranayake
Intercooperation
92/2 D S Senanayake Mawatha
Colombo 8
tel: 94-1-691215; fax: 94-1-687467/695979
telex: 22151 or 21208 HPT CE attn: Intercooperation

In Uganda: Dr. John Aluma
Head, Forestry Department, Makerere University
PO Box 7062, Kampala

In the UK: Sustainable Agriculture Programme
IIED, 3 Endsleigh Street, London WC1H 0DD
tel: 071-388-2117; fax: 071-388-2826
telex: 261681 EASCAN G

In Vietnam: Lê Minit Tuê
c/o Interforest AB
PO Box 36, Hanoi
tel: 010-84-42-53236; fax: 010-84-42-52542
telex: 411301 MOF VI

In Zimbabwe: Saiti Makuku
Forestry Research Centre
PO Box 595 HG
Highlands, Harare
tel: 263-4-46878/9; fax: 263-4-795557
telex: 22446 ZW

APPENDIX B

PRA: START, STUMBLE, SELF-CORRECT, SHARE

Participatory Rural Appraisal is a label. More and more people are adopting it, and calling what they do PRA. More and more influential organizations are requesting or requiring that PRA be carried out.

This brings dangers and opportunities.

The dangers are that the label will be used or claimed for activities where behaviour and attitudes are not participatory; that these activities will do badly; and that good PRA will be discredited. There is a danger too that the demand for training in PRA will so outstrip good supply that people will claim to be PRA trainers when they have no direct personal experience of good PRA. This has already happened.

The opportunities are hard to assess but look big. Time will show. Perhaps we have in good PRA one among a family of approaches for reversing centralization, standardization, and top-down development; and for enabling and empowering rural communities and the poor to do more of their own analysis, to take command more of their lives and resources, and to improve their wellbeing as they define it.

So what is the core of good PRA?

We will all have different answers. It is more important to ask the question, and to puzzle and puzzle about good answers, than to have one right answer. It is more important for each person and each group to invent and adapt their own approach, methods, sequences and combinations than to adopt a ready-made manual or model. Let a thousand flowers bloom (and why only a thousand?), and let them be flowers which bloom better and better, and spread their seeds.

Here is one personal set of answers. If you read them, criticize them. Reject them. Think out your own, from your own ideas and experience.

In the words of the one-sentence manual

'Use your own best judgement at all times'

The core of good PRA is our behaviour and attitudes.

It involves:

- being self-aware and self-critical
- embracing error
- handing over the stick
- sitting, listening and learning
- improvising, inventing, adapting
- using our own best judgement at all times

So we can ask:

- who lectures? who holds the stick? whose finger wags?
- whose knowledge, analysis and priorities count?

Ours? Theirs, as we think they should be? Or theirs as they freely express them?

Good PRA is empowering, not extractive.

Good PRA makes mistakes, learns from them, and so is self-improving.

Good PRA spreads and improves on its own.

So START. Do not wait. Get on with it. Relax. Try things. Learn by doing. Fail forwards. Experiment. Ask - what went well? What went badly? What can we learn? How can we do better? How can we help others to do better?

Remember the three pillars:

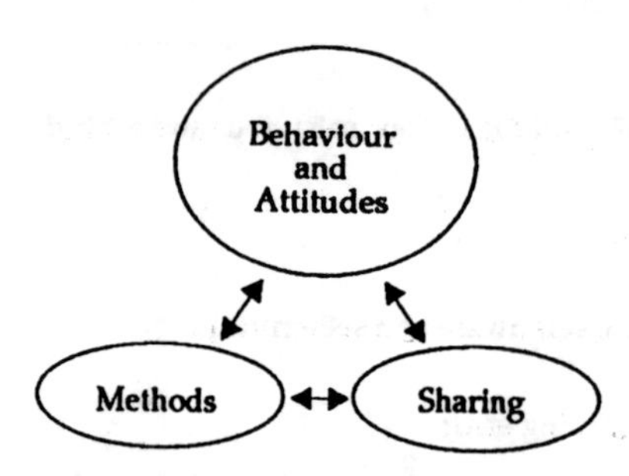

Done well, PRA becomes self-improving and self-spreading: self-improving through critical awareness, embracing error, and learning what works; and self-spreading through sharing.

Start with behaviour and attitudes. Ours. And use the methods at once to help.

Or start with a method, and observe and reflect on your behaviour and attitudes as you use it. Relax. Listen. Keep quiet. Allow fun. Learn. And learn how to do better.

PRA is what we make of it. It is a potential, not a panacea. If you do not like it, leave it. No one will mind. It is not for everyone. But if you like it, and use it, share it and help others to share.

Have a go. Why not?